CONTENTS

Hello and Welcome!

Hello and welcome to *Magpie Annual 1976*!

We hope very much that you enjoy being reminded of some of the items that have been on the programme and that you find in this book all the other ingredients that you expect in a *Magpie Annual* – puzzles and competitions and things to make and do and features that make you want to go out and discover more for yourself.

Magpie birds are well known for finding interesting things and hoarding them for the future. Jenny, Mick and Doug are like this, too, always on the look-out for interesting items which they can then show you. It's a good idea to find out as much as possible and to hoard any bits and pieces of information in your mind. You never know when they'll come in handy, and sometimes you notice that a group of them all fit together like a jigsaw puzzle and suddenly you know quite a lot about something.

Jenny, Mick and Doug always love to get your letters telling them what you've been doing and finding out about, and which of the programme items have interested you most; so do keep writing to them. Meanwhile, here are some pictures from their own favourite items throughout the year.

Douglas has ridden horses all over the world for Magpie—in Africa, in the Lebanon, at Calgary and in the studio (you remember that Japanese horse that galloped on the spot if you pressed the right button on its neck). Here he is practising bareback riding at the Robert Brothers Circus in Cambridge.

The first film story Jenny ever did for Magpie was at the London Zoo when she helped wash down an elephant. That was really hard work and she was quite happy when her next visit to London Zoo was simply to look at the pandas. Pandas were by no means the only animals that you saw on Magpie. For instance, you watched Alison Staines win the Magpie Challenge Trophy at Alexandra Palace Pets Show with her cavie "Cornish Princess".

And Martin Lacey, as always, regularly popped into the studio when he had interesting animals from his zoo at Sherwood to show you. Here are some 8 week old, ferocious-looking lion cubs.

Pop Spot is one of your favourite regular items. Many pop groups have been seen on the programme. Among the more interesting stars that you saw was Tom Paxton.

And the exotic Agar Mmba from West Africa.

Mick had a look at more serious musical studies, too, when he spent a day at the Yehudi Menuhin School of Music. Here, children specially talented at music can concentrate on learning their instruments while studying normal school subjects too. Here, Mick has a cello lesson from Tonino Lysy aged 12. And this is Nicola Hurton aged 15 who plays the guitar as well as the violin.

Jenny with some of the seven deadly sins—Gluttony, Sloth, Avarice, Lust, Envy, Greed and Adultery—puppets made by Jennifer Carey for the Royal Shakespeare Theatre's production of Dr Faustus.

What on earth does Puff do all day when he's not on Magpie? Jenny went along to Pauline Voss's riding school at Banstead where Puff and his 42 stable-mates live, to investigate his daily routine.

He makes sure he's up by 7.30, because that's when he's given breakfast. Then his stable is mucked out; the droppings and wet wood-chips (used for his bedding this year because straw is so expensive) are shovelled up and taken away in a barrow. Then the edges of the bedding are put in the centre of the stable and new wood-chips are spread around the outside. He's also given a fresh bucket of water.

Then he's taken out of the stable, tied up with a quick-release knot and he's ready for grooming. First his hooves are picked out so that he won't develop "thrush"—this might happen if mud and stones were left in his hooves. A dandy brush is used to clean his coat of any mud; then he is brushed over with a body brush.

Now Puff is ready to be tacked up for his first ride. Jenny watched this being done in the indoor riding school where Puff rides when the weather is bad. He wears a specially fitted saddle and a jointed snaffle bridle.

At lunchtime, he nibbles at his haynet. Then he might go out on another ride in the afternoon before having his evening meal at about 5.00. At 5.30 his night rug is put on and he is left to his own

PUFF

You can make your pony's diet go a bit further by supplementing it with food like mashed potatoes, turnips and carrots; by covering him with a rug (he'll get hungrier if he's cold); and by always putting hay in a net to avoid waste. The important thing, though, is not to buy a pony if he's going to be too expensive to keep properly.

devices until 8.30 when Pauline comes to pat him and say goodnight.

Each winter Puff and the 5,000 or so other ponies in Britain face something of a crisis because of the enormous cost of feeding them. Grain, oats, bran and hay are all shooting up in price and some people who have bought ponies when the summer's grass is cheap find they must sell them in the winter. Each month Puff eats 6 bales of hay (that costs £12), $\frac{1}{2}$ cwt of bran (£2.45), $\frac{1}{2}$ cwt oats (£2.20) and 2 cwt pony nuts (£8). So it costs about £25 a month to feed Puff, and each year the price increases.

Puff was in and out of the studio last year quite a bit. He also got out and about on some film stories. One he enjoyed very much was at Grange Farm Sports Centre in Essex where Jo Hills runs one of the country's 200 riding schools for disabled children. Before joining the school, pupils are assessed by a panel of doctors and riding instructors so that they can receive the tuition most suitable for their handicap. The handicapped child replaces his disabled legs with the good ones of a pony and riding becomes a sport which he can enjoy just as much as normal children—and he can become just as good. And, of course, doing the exercise to help your handicap on a horse is much less of a chore than if you do it on your own—so the children benefit in that way, too.

There is some special equipment at the school—such as "ladder reins" which are reins with straps across them to help children with muscular problems grip the reins; and mounting ramps so that a child on crutches or in a wheel chair can simply swing himself straight on to the horse. But the object of the riding is to help the child overcome his handicap by teaching him to use special techniques, not by using artificial aids—so the special equipment is used as little as possible.

It was clear to Puff and Mick that the children were having a good time—and being helped, too.

Jason by Joyce Stranger (*Carousel*, 25p)
An adventure story set in the Highlands about a Labrador called Jason, who rescues his young master and reunites him with his father in more ways than one.

What do steak and kidney pie, a cake, a pullover and a jug of custard have in common? The answer is that the main ingredient of each of them comes from farms. From cows come steak for the pie and milk for the custard. Wheat supplies the flour that goes in the cake and sheep provide the wool that makes the pullover. Many other things that we use everyday come from the animals and crops that are raised on farms. They are very important places so last year Magpie paid regular visits to one farm to see what happens.

Elm Tree Farm covers 260 acres of Northamptonshire and is run by Mr and Mrs Threadgold. It is a mixed farm which means Mr Threadgold keeps animals as well as growing crops. He has a herd of ninety-two Friesian cows plus one bull whose name is Tom Roy Tankard. Each day the cows produce 200 gallons of milk which is collected by an enormous tanker. The cows are milked twice a day for ten months of the year, then they rest for eight weeks. They must each have one calf every year, so that they can produce milk.

Even in the most modern dairies, a lot of work has to be done by hand. For instance, the cows' udders must be washed before milking begins so that the milk is clean and pure. When the cows are relaxed 'clusters' are put on their udders and the milk is drawn out by a pump, up a tube into a large glass jar. It takes about six minutes to milk a cow and the farmer can milk five at a time. While being milked the cows are given a measured amount of cattle cake. When it is nearly full, each jar empties and the milk is pumped through a system of glass pipes then into the bulk tank in the dairy next door. The milk is kept there and cooled to keep it fresh. After the milking session the whole system is thoroughly cleaned out.

Most of the cows have their calves between September and December. After the first three days of their lives the calves are separated from their mothers. They are kept indoors while they learn to walk and feed themselves. Mr Threadgold's weaning technique is to make a mixture of milk and water in a bucket. Then he puts a finger in the bucket and allows the calves to suck his finger. After a couple of days they begin to drink by themselves. They drink about four pints of milk mixed with one pint of water, twice a day.

TREE FARM

Half the young cows will become milking cows as soon as they have calved. The other half are later sold for beef in the market. In the summer the cows eat grass in the fields, but in winter they live in the cowshed, feeding on hay, straw, carrots, cow cake and protein.

Mr Threadgold has a flock of 187 sheep as well as four rams, and last year they produced 290 lambs, many of which go to the market for meat. In June, the sheep are sheared for their wool. Shearing is a skilled job, but an experienced shearer can shear up to 200 sheep a day. The fleece goes to the wool merchant, then to the Wool Marketing Board and then to the manufacturer who mills and spins it.

Mr Threadgold's crops include barley, wheat and oats and he sows them in the early autumn. Before sowing the seeds, he must plough the field to create a good feed-bed for the crops and turn the old stubble under the ground. Mr Threadgold can plough up to ten acres a day with his reversible plough. When the field is ploughed, a disc harrow is towed behind a tractor to make the soil loose and ready for the seeds.

Then the seeds can be sown from the seed drill. This, too, is towed from a tractor. As the seeds drop from the drill, they are covered by a harrow that is pulled along behind.

During the summer Mr Threadgold has to cut the grass so that he has hay for his cows in the winter. The grass is ready to cut when it begins to die off but still has seeds inside it.

Three days after the hay has been cut it is tossed about to let the air and moisture out and to speed up the drying process. Speed is extremely important as the quicker the hay is dried, the better it is. When the hay is dry, it is ready for baling. The baler gathers the dry hay in at one end and drops out firm, tied-up bales at the other end. They are caught in groups of seven by the bale sledge and when full the gate opens and leaves the bales behind ready for stacking. A trailer collects the bales and brings them to the farmyard where they are piled into the Dutch barn; a bale elevator is used to get them to the top. Seven thousand bales keep Mr Threadgold's animals through the winter.

These are just a few of the jobs that Mr Threadgold must do on his farm throughout the year. His is not the sort of work that can be done from nine to five. His day normally begins at six in the morning and ends at 6.30 in the evening, but the hours are even longer during harvesting and when animals are being born.

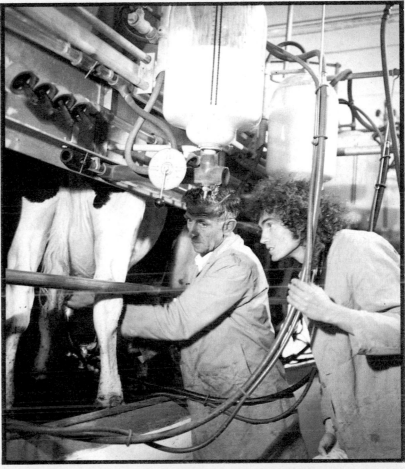

Wherever there's mud, there are likely to be animal tracks. If you keep your eyes skinned, you'll notice them. In the country you might be lucky enough to see the track of a deer or a badger. In the town the tracks are more likely to be of dogs and cats and birds – but there are lots of different types of those. You can take plaster casts of the tracks you see. Then you can collect them and try to identify the animals which made the tracks. The things you need to take casts of tracks will fit into a small bag: a packet of plaster of Paris, a bottle of clean water, a plastic

bowl and a spoon. Plus a tin or piece of strong card large enough to encircle the track, a knife and old newspaper.

The first thing to do when you see an interesting track is to remove any leaves or bits of mud that may have fallen into it. Do this very carefully or you'll damage the details of the track. Sometimes a good blow gets rid of the debris. Or a pair of tweezers may help.

Rabbit

Birds

Moorhen

Grey squirrel

Fox

TRACKS

time looking for other tracks, or, if your track is fresh, seeing if the animal reappears.

When the plaster is dry, cut out the clod of soil beneath the track and completely remove the soil and plaster. Take away the card or tin and pack the whole cast in newspaper for taking home.

In the bowl, mix the plaster of Paris with enough water to make it creamy, not runny. Press the tin or card into the soil around the track and carefully pour in the plaster. You'll avoid getting air bubbles if you pour it onto the side of the track. Cover the track with about 1½ inches of plaster. Now you'll have about 20 minutes while the plaster dries. You could occupy the

When you're home, gently wash the soil from the plaster to reveal the track. You could colour its background and round its side write the date and place that you found it and the type of animal it belongs to. See how many different tracks you can find.

GATROYD JAN 1975

...ok

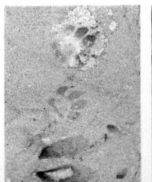

Badger cub and fallow deer

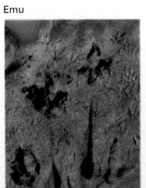

Emu

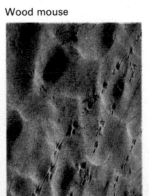

Wood mouse

Rabbit crossed by fox

CLOCKING

The word clock really means a bell and there was a time when clocks had no hands or dials. They told the time only by striking a bell. (You can see one of these old clocks at Salisbury Cathedral.) But when people talk about Big Ben meaning the clock at Westminster, they are not quite accurate. Big Ben is in fact the name of the bell which strikes on the hour in the belfry of Westminster clock tower.

Jenny found this out when she visited Big Ben, which is often heard but seldom seen. There was a clock—and a bell —in the Palace of Westminster long before Big Ben was installed in 1859; the first clock tower was built there by Edward 1 in 1288. It was pulled down in 1707 and members of Parliament did without a clock tower. But when the Houses of Parliament were being rebuilt after the fire which destroyed them in 1834, they thought they would like a clock again. The office of works promised them 'a noble

Big Ben

clock, indeed a king of clocks'. Big Ben's clock is certainly very fine. It was designed by E. B. Denison (later Lord Grimthorpe) and E. J. Dent (although only Denison's name is inscribed on the clock). Its main feature—invented by the designers—is the gravity escapement; the escapement in a clock is the mechanism which regulates the swing of the pendulum. Most tower or turret clocks now have gravity escapements.

Big Ben itself caused more problems than the clock. It was cast out of 16 tons of metal in two furnaces near Stockton-on-Tees. Then began its journey to London; it came by rail to West Hartlepool, then by a boat (which it badly damaged by falling too quickly on its deck). Then from the Port of London it was pulled to Westminster by sixteen white horses. Many crowds gathered to marvel at Big Ben, but it was found to be damaged—a crack four feet long had appeared. There was

Jenny inside the clock face of Big Ben

Inside the mechanism room

IN

Noon
Greenwich Mean Time

p.m.
Berlin

a.m.
Chicago

a.m.
New York

BIG BEN Facts and Figures

The clock **tower** rises 316 feet from the Thames. You must climb 334 steps to reach the belfry.

Each of the clock's **4 faces** is 23 feet in diameter and contains over 300 pieces of glass. The faces are washed every 3 years. The figures are 2 feet long. Under each face is the inscription 'Domine salvam fac reginam nostram Victoria primam' (O Lord, save our Queen Victoria the first).

The minute **hands** are made of copper sheet and are each 14 feet long, weigh 2 cwt and travel 100 miles a year at their tip.

The hour hands are made of gunmetal and are each 9 feet long.

The clock's **pendulum** is 13 feet long, weighs 6 cwt and beats every 2 seconds. Its mechanism weighs about 5 tons.

Big Ben itself is 9 feet in diameter and 7½ feet high. It weighs exactly 13 tons, 10 cwts, 3 qtrs and 15 lbs.

The 4 quarter **bells** vary in size from 3¾ feet in diameter to 6 feet. The notes they sound are G, F, E and B.

The total cost of the clock and bells up to 1889—£22,000.

Big Ben being dragged through London by horses

Peking
p.m.

Fiji
p.m.

Aleutian Islands
next day
a.m.

Moscow
p.m.

Bangkok
p.m.

nothing for it but to melt Big Ben and start again.

A slightly smaller version was made at Whitechapel in London and in October 1858 was hauled up the clock tower and suspended on massive iron girders in the belfry.

The hands for the clock were a bit late in arriving. But at last all the parts for the clock were assembled and Big Ben was in its place ready to strike at the right moment—and on 11 July, for the first time, Londoners were able to put their watches right by Big Ben. Then, two months later, disaster struck. Ben cracked again. For four years Big Ben was silent while bitter dispute raged about whose fault it was and why it had happened. At last a simple remedy was found. Ben was given a quarter of a turn so that the hammer struck in a different place, and the hammer itself was lightened. Ben's crack remains plainly visible.

"As old as Time itself". How old is that? What is time? These are very difficult questions but worth thinking about. You don't have to be able to put the answers into words, though, to understand the importance of being able to tell the time—to be able to measure it. Imagine what would happen if we couldn't tell the time—it would be pure coincidence if two people ever met together in the same place, let alone if, say, a football crowd all arrived at the right moment for kick-off.

Even in ancient times, people realised the value of being able to measure time and they devised primitive methods of doing so. The earliest timing device consisted simply of a stick stuck in the ground. The time was then told by the length or direction of shadow cast by the stick—for the Egyptians and Babylonians who used these methods understood that the sun regularly rose and fell and was followed by a period of darkness. By measuring the shadows, they could therefore tell what part of the day it was.

The earliest shadow clock known—one that actually has markings on it, was made in Egypt in about 1500 BC. The divisions on it are unequal because the shadows move more quickly at the beginning and end of the day than they do nearer noon. You can make your own shadow clock by sticking a stick in the ground

outside and marking the position of its shadows at hourly intervals.

You can make some of the other timing devices that people used in ancient times, too. Make a water clock, for instance: pierce a small hole in the bottom of a tin or plastic beaker and stand it on a jamjar. Fill the tin or beaker with water, then mark on the jamjar the water level at each hour. You can make a sand clock in the same way, using sand instead of water. Sand clocks are still used, of course, as egg-timers. They used to be used in churches, too, for the preacher to time the length of his sermon.

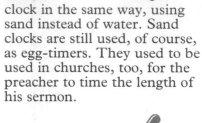

If you keep your eyes open you may notice an old sundial on your local church. There is a fine Saxon one, for example, on Kirkdale Church in Yorkshire dating from about the time of William the Conqueror. There's another on Bewcastle Cross in Cumberland and on Bishopstone Church in Sussex. And, of course, some people have ornamental sundials in their gardens.

Alfred the Great is thought to have used a candle clock to

keep track of his working day; he had a candle which burned away in exactly four hours if it was kept inside a wooden lantern away from draughts. You can make a candle clock by taking two candles of the same size and lighting one of them. Then, at regular intervals mark where it has burnt down to on the other candle. Then light the other candle and see if it burns at the same rate.

The fabulous astronomical clock designed by Dondi of Padua in the fourteenth century, recently reconstructed and now exhibited in the Science Museum, London

The first mechanical clocks were made in England in about 1370. One of the oldest still in existence is the one in Salisbury Cathedral. None of these mechanical clocks were very accurate, so they were seldom fitted with a minute hand. After the invention of the pendulum clock, though, in the middle of the seventeenth century, the added accuracy made it worthwhile fitting minutes hands and even second hands. The swinging pendulum controls the rate at which the clock's hands move and because a pendulum swings more evenly than a hanging weight which is influenced by the pull of gravity, these were more correct.

In medieval times, clocks used to be made as a sideline by blacksmiths. It was not until much later that clock-making became a profession in its own right. One of the best known English clock-makers was Thomas Tompion (1639–1713), whose clocks today are collector's pieces. Tompion also did a lot of pioneer work on accurate watches. Before the middle of the seventeenth century, people tended to wear watches as jewellery—for decoration only. Queen Elizabeth I, for instance, had quite a collection of ornamental watches.

Nowadays, most of us wear watches and expect them to be accurate, although we don't usually complain if a watch loses a minute or two a day.

For astronomers, though, and for space stations and some scientists, absolute accuracy is essential, and inventors are continually trying to find ways of making clocks keep better time. The most advanced clocks in the world are quartz crystal clocks and atomic clocks—both light years away from the original shadow clocks!

Workings of the Salisbury Cathedral clock

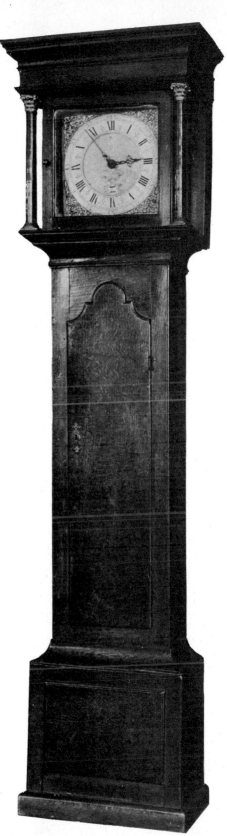

Grandfather clock

The Incredible Adventures of Professor Branestawm by Norman Hunter (illustrated by Heath Robinson) (*Puffin, 30p*)
Very funny story about the absent-minded professor, with delightfully eccentric drawings by Heath Robinson.

What's in a NAME

Just as today there is a craze for wearing badges bearing the name of a favourite pop star or football club, so in Victorian times there was a craze for wearing brooches bearing one's own name. Below are some of the Victorian name brooches that you saw on Magpie last year, together with the derivations or meanings of the names.

Fanny is the diminutive of Frances, which appeared in England in the Tudor period. In Elizabethan times, when it was a popular name with the aristocracy, it was often shortened to Frank, even for girls, and at that time it was spelt in the same way as the boys' name.

Dorothy comes from a Greek name meaning 'gift of God'. It wasn't used in England until the end of the fifteenth century when it was pronounced without the 'h' and was often spelt 'Dorate'. Diminutives of Dorothy include Doll, Dot and Dodo.

Edith comes from the Old English name Eadgyth meaning 'rich' (*ead*) 'war' (*gyth*). The name was popular throughout the Middle Ages, then it almost died out, but was revived in Victorian times.

Madeline comes from Hebrew and means 'woman of Magdala'. Madeline can also be spelt Magdalen—or Madeleine, which is the French form of the name.

Stella is the Latin for 'star'. The Elizabethan poet Sir Philip Sidney wrote a famous sequence of sonnets called 'Astrophel to Stella'.

Bert is the diminutive form of Albert which comes from the Old German words *athal*, meaning 'noble' and *berhta*, 'bright'. There were Alberts mentioned in Domesday Book, but the name became really popular after Queen Victoria's marriage to Albert. In America, Albert is usually abbreviated to Al. In England, Bert can also be the diminutive of other names ending in -bert, such as Cuthbert, Hubert and Herbert.

Mabel was a favourite Victorian name, which is a shortened form of Amabel, derived from the Latin word *amabilis* meaning 'lovable'.

Lizzie is the diminutive of Elizabeth, which comes from the Hebrew word *elisheba* meaning 'oath of God'. In medieval times, Elizabeth was transformed into Isabel. The name has been very popular ever since the reign of Elizabeth I. There are a great many diminutives of Elizabeth, including Betsy, Betty, Bess, Eliza, Tetty, Libby and Beth. This brooch shows Lizzie in the form of a monogram.

Emma means 'whole' or 'universal'. It was introduced into England by Emma, daughter of Richard I, Duke of Normandy. She married first King Ethelred the Unready and second in 1017, King Cnut. The name was very common in Norman times and has remained popular almost ever since.

Something else to do
Make a monogram from your own name, using the Lizzie brooch as an example.
And
Look at these portraits of American presidents and draw your own face using the letters of your name.

Annie is the diminutive of Anna, which is derived from the Hebrew name Hannah, meaning 'favoured by God'. Anna was introduced to the West from Russia by the wife of Henri I of France. The name has been popular in England since the sixteenth century and Annie has been a name in its own right since Victorian times.

Harriet is the English form of the French name Henriette, which in turn is derived from the male name Henry, meaning 'ruler of the house'. The name Henriette was brought to England by Henriette Maria, French wife of Charles I.

Make your own name brooch!
Twist a pipe cleaner or a length of ⅛" guage wire into the shape of your name, attach it to an attractive backing such as velvet, and make a clasp from a safety pin.

A Child's Book of Verses by Robert Louis Stevenson (*Oxford University Press*, £2.00) The famous collection of poems by Robert Louis Stevenson, first published in 1885 and now beautifully illustrated by Brian Wildsmith.

DUCHAMPS and the CHRISTMAS DINNER 🎄

by
John Hartley

At five o'clock on Christmas morning no light shone from the hundred windows of the Chateau de Grand-Montparnasse. The dark bulk of the ancient castle loomed behind Duchamps as he strode over the frost-crisp lawns, between the frozen fountains, across the terrace with its paving of black and white marble octagons, and down through the curving stone balustrades towards the woods beyond. As his boots crunched through the frosty longer grass the yellow light from his candle lantern gleamed on their bobbing buckles and on the silver buttons of his greatcoat. It glimmered too on the meat cleaver which hung from his belt, its blade now too chipped for the fine work of the kitchen and suitable only for chopping wood.

On Christmas mornings Duchamps, master-chef to the Duc de Grand-Montparnasse, liked to be his own woodcutter. On this most important day, even the holly for the Duke's table had to be selected by him personally. For this was the

day of the Christmas Dinner. At eight o'clock precisely, forty-nine guests would sit down to a meal which was famed throughout the great houses of France. A meal of delicacies and surprises. A meal of unsurpassed distinction. Once, six years before, the King himself had eaten Duchamps' Christmas dinner. And on another occasion the great Charbonnier, chef of the Hotel Perigord in Paris, had visited the kitchens to watch the preparations ''so as to learn something from Duchamps, my former pupil''.

Duchamps remembered as he came to the birch trees that it was Charbonnier who had first created the dish that would be tonight's great surprise: terrine of thrushes! Earlier that year it had been the talk of Paris that Maitre Orgueil, His Majesty's personal chef, had offered Charbonnier a purse of gold for the recipe. The offer had, of course, been refused. Chefs do not sell their secrets, and no gentleman would attempt to buy them. Tonight's dish would be Duchamps' own original invention. Lavoisin the gamekeeper had already netted a dozen song thrushes and redwings and they were caged outside the kitchen. By noon the pie would be made.

Inside the copse Duchamps held his lantern high until he found a good, thickly berried holly bush. He hung the lantern on one branch, his greatcoat on another, and selected a third clustered with bright berries. He swung back the cleaver to make the first cut, but stopped with his arm in mid-air. There had come suddenly from behind him the lovely sound of a bird singing. He let the axe fall to his side and turned towards the fluting, liquid song. Its thrilling sound soared and trembled in the air almost without a pause, and soon Duchamps located the singer. High on a bare birch tree, silhouetted against the pale eyelash of moon which still hung in the dawn sky, was a slim little bird. It stood erect, head thrown back and throat swelling with the rich music of its song. The bird was unmistakeable to a countryman, even one like Duchamps who had spent so many years in towns. It was a song thrush.

He listened for fully five minutes, perhaps six, before the thrush ended its song and flew low through the trees away from him. Afterwards he stood for a while in the new silence, thinking. Then he turned, chopped down the holly branch with a few quick strokes, grabbed the lantern (which blew out) and the greatcoat (which he did not bother to put on) and hurried back up the hill to the chateau with the holly over his shoulder. In the huge basement kitchen, work was just beginning. Madame Sabot the pastrycook stood at the long scrubbed table with her floury hands delving in a yellow bowl. Chantal, the general maid, was plucking a guineafowl in the corner. Madeleine the kitchenmaid was sleepily cracking walnuts and resisting the temptation to eat them all. Clarence the butler-valet was sharpening and polishing a heap of silver knives. Alain, the cook-apprentice, was balancing on a chair to take a ham down from its ceiling hook when the door crashed open behind him. They all stopped, astonished, as Duchamps stumbled breathlessly into the room with the prickly holly entangling his legs.

''Good morning everyone,'' he panted. ''Happy Christmas.''

''Er . . . Happy Christmas, Monsieur Duchamps,'' they said — except for Clarence, who was an old friend of Duchamps and called him by his first name.

"Well, don't stop working," said Duchamps. "We have lots to do. In fact we have even more to do than you thought. Ha ha!" He rubbed his hands together. "Madeleine — release the thrushes! Let them fly away!"

They all stopped again and stared at him. Release the thrushes? But the terrine was to be the *pièce de résistance* of the dinner. For weeks they had been discussing the recipe. For days Madame Sabot had been considering the exact texture of the piecrust. Already that morning Alain had gathered Duchamps' selection of fresh herbs. Had Monsieur Duchamps gone mad? Or could it be — no, surely not   that he was not sure he could bring off the recipe successfully? All these things they thought, and some of them they said. So Duchamps told them of the beautiful song thrush, and how he felt he could not on this day of all days make a sacrifice of such birds. Not even for the pleasure of his master and his noble guests.

"Then what are we to do, Monsieur?" wailed Madame Sabot, who was really quite near to tears. Duchamps raised his hand for silence.

"My friends," he said, "we are going to practise a little deception." Madeleine was sent at once to fetch a shoulder of veal and some chicken livers. Alain was given a new list of herbs and spices. Madame Sabot was kissed on both cheeks and told to continue with her excellent pastry. And Duchamps took off his coat, rolled up his sleeves, put on his chef's apron and hat, and set to work. By half-past ten, he was satisfied with the taste of his fake mixture. By eleven o'clock the big blue and white terrine dish was lined with bacon, filled with Duchamps' concoction, sealed with pastry under the lid and placed in the brick oven for its first cooking. At eleven forty-five it was removed. Everyone tasted it. Suggestions were made. A bay leaf was added. And a tablespoon of Madeira. Some veal stock in which russet apples had been simmered was poured on top. Then the dish was placed in the hands of Madame Sabot. One hour later it was again removed from the oven, its glazed crust glowing a golden brown and its fragrant aroma filling the kitchen.

"Violà!" cried Alain. "Monsieur Duchamps' terrine of thrush — without thrushes." And everyone laughed with pleasure and relief.

Throughout the day preparations continued. The ovens filled and the dishes multiplied. Extra waitresses arrived from the village, and were rehearsed in their duties by Clarence. As eight o'clock approached, the whole kitchen was a flurry of nervous excitement. Upstairs the dining hall was laid with silver and porcelain and sparkling glass, the candlesticks decorated with springs of Duchamps' holly. Huge logs blazed in the open fireplace as Duchamps and Clarence made their final tour of the table. Clarence polished a glass or two. Duchamps added a few black olives to a bowl already full. Each knew what the other was thinking, and both knew that everyone below was thinking the same. Would the false pie deceive the Duke and his guests, whose carriage wheels and horses' hooves could be heard even now on the gravel drive?

At eight the Duke led everyone into the dining room, recited the traditional Grace of the Ducs de Grand-

Montparnasse, and invited them to sit down. Duchamps carried in the first tureen and proudly announced it. The noise and laughter rose as the guests sipped the delicious cream and cucumber soup, savoured the wines, tasted the salmon flakes and asked for second helpings of the tomato salad. Chantal, Clarence and Duchamps glanced at each other tensely as they worked. Then the time came. Madeleine brought the great dish from the kitchen and handed it to Duchamps on its silver tray. Duchamps, holding the tray aloft, carried it slowly the length of the room to the Duke's seat at the head of the table. His tongue felt dry. His voice wavered.

"My Lord Duke, my Lord Bishop, my Lords, my Ladies, gentlemen of France . . . Terrine of Thrushes."

There was a murmur of appreciation and one or two people applauded. Duchamps set the dish down in front of the Duke and Clarence handed him the knife. But to their shock, the Duke did not take it. Instead he pushed the dish away and rose to his feet. There was immediate silence as he began to speak.

"My friends," he said, "all of you know that Duchamps here is one of the greatest of all chefs." Duchamps felt his face reddening. "He is also, as you are, my friend. He has served me loyally for twenty-two years. Nothing I am about to say is any dishonour to him. But — I cannot eat this fine dish he has prepared for us." He turned to the two servants as he spoke. "You see, this morning after I had dressed and Clarence had left me, a most amazing and lovely thing happened. I was sitting in my room before breakfast, reading as I usually do, when I heard a sound more beautiful than any Christmas choir. In fact it *was* such a choir, but a choir of birds! I looked out, and there on my window sill were, well, it must have been a dozen thrushes, singing with all their might. They sang and sang, and it seemed to me like a Christmas gift from Nature herself it was so beautiful. And now I do not have it in my heart to eat such creatures. But Duchamps, Clarence, offer some to our guests. They did not hear the choir, and they are hungry!"

It was no good. Even though the scent of the pie was wafting through the dining room, every guest followed their host's example. There was an uncomfortable silence. Then Chantal, unable to contain herself, began to giggle. Clarence hushed her up, but was unable to stop himself smiling too at the turn events had taken. Duchamps, who had been overwhelmed by the Duke's speech, bit his lip to suppress a grin. The Duke noticed.

"I am glad you are taking this so calmly, Duchamps," he said. "I thought you would be very disappointed."

"My Lord," said Duchamps, "I have a secret I wish to tell you. But first, eat a little of the terrine and I promise that no thrush will pass your lips." He offered him a morsel. The Duke looked at his guests, shrugged, and ate the piece. But then his face angered.

"Come, Duchamps, enough of this. The thrush pie is delicious but I say I will not eat it." Then Duchamps, coming close to his master's ear, asked permission to explain everything to him and all the guests.

"Very well," said the Duke sternly, and Duchamps

nervously and briefly told his tale, with Chantal and Clarence nodding confession to their own part in the pretence. The terrine was duly served to the Duke and every guest, and their amusement turned to wonderment as they tasted it.

"I don't believe him," shouted someone. "I've tasted Charbonnier's thrush pie and this is even better."

"Duchamps," said the Duke, "do you swear that your story is true, and this pie is made without a single thrush?"

"I swear it my Lord," replied Duchamps.

"Friends," announced the Duke, "Duchamps does not lie. Is he not the finest of all chefs?"

"And you are the finest of all hosts," said the Comtesse de Saint Salvadou, at which everyone applauded.

As Duchamps walked back down the long hall the clapping and congratulation continued and five or six people turned to shake his hand. The only dissent came from the Bishop, who complained that the pie was not big enough for him to have a third helping.

It was one o'clock in the morning before the last guests left, and all agreed that it was quite the finest Christmas dinner they had ever eaten, and that the thrush terrine (for so they still called it) was an exquisite masterpiece, and that the Duke could not afford to lose such a brilliant chef. As the carriages jingled down the drive the servants sat in their candlelit kitchen and Duchamps opened a bottle of Vouvray that he had purchased for the occasion. He poured a glass for everyone, and thanked them for their hard and successful work on such an important day. "It went well," he said finally. "Thank you all." They were mostly too tired to feel like eating, but Clarence had some roast guinea-fowl and a piece of bread, and everyone helped to finish Madame Sabot's vast bilberry pie. Alain shyly proposed a toast to Monsieur Duchamps, and said that however long he was a chef he would always remember that day. Everyone else said they would remember it too, except Madeleine who was yawning. It was nearly bedtime. There were more meals to cook tomorrow.

"Well my friends," said Duchamps, "I think we should drink one more toast with what remains of the wine. I drink to those beautiful songbirds, the thrushes." They raised their glasses.

"The thrushes," they laughed.

"The thrushes!" cried Madeleine suddenly, jumping to her feet with her hands to her cheeks. "Oh, la, Monsieur Duchamps, I am so sorry. We were so busy this morning that I forgot to let them out of their cage. I will go and do it now, sir. At once."

TOTE BAG

You need: a large sheet of newspaper; a pair of scissors; ½ yard of tough material (eg canvas, hessian, corduroy, or denim); pins; a felt tip pen; a ruler; glue; a needle; button thread; 2 pieces of bamboo, each about 15 inches long.

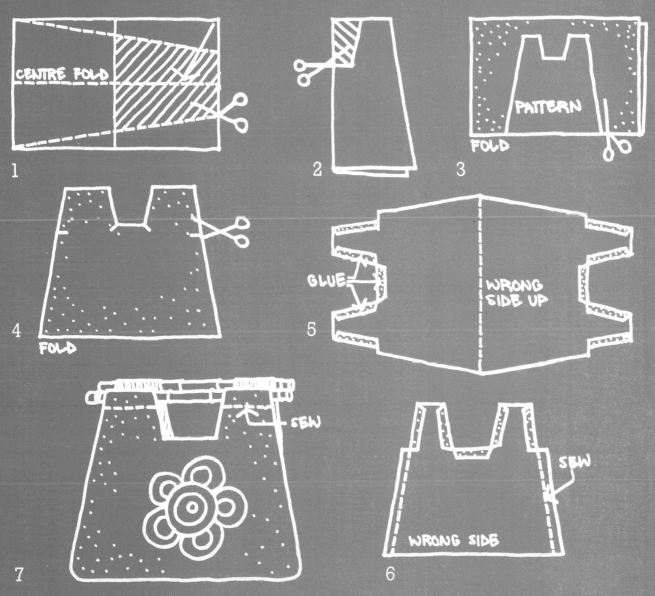

1. Fold a double page of newspaper in half, open it out again, then bend two of its corners to the centre. Cut out the shaded area.   **2.** Fold in half the piece you have cut out. Using a felt tip pen and a ruler, draw the bag's handles and cut them out.   **3.** Open out your pattern as shown in the diagram. Pin it on the *folded* material and cut the material out.   **4.** Snip notches on either side about 1½ inches below the handles and at the corners of the 'neck'.   **5.** Open out the bag so its wrong side faces you and glue down the seams round the handles and neck.   **6.** Fold the bag together so its right sides are face to face and sew the side seams from the bottoms to the notches.   **7.** Turn the bag the right way out. Fold the handles over the pieces of bamboo and sew very close to the wood. Decorate your tote bag with leather or felt or whatever takes your fancy.

YOUR THOUSANDS £

When the Magpie Appeal closed last year the total you had collected was over seventy-two thousand pounds. This had risen by the end of March to over £86,000 and the money was still coming in. Jenny, Mick and Doug were delighted by the enormous sums of money that you sent in. But their pleasure will be multiplied many times over by the children who, because of your generosity, will be able to have a holiday. For last year's Appeal was for children who are in some way handicapped—physically, mentally or socially—and therefore find it difficult to go on holiday unless they have a special holiday home to go to.

Everyone needs a holiday, at least once a year. Holidays are times when we can do what we really want to do, and they give a refreshing break in the daily routine of our lives. If you can't have a holiday, for whatever reason, it's pretty tough luck.

That's what Jenny, Mick and Doug thought when they launched the Magpie Appeal. With the help of an organisation which helps administrate holiday homes for handicapped children, it asked you for money to equip various homes throughout the country. The main project, though, was to equip a home called after 'Magpie', which would welcome seventeen children at any one time. Over the course of a year, this would mean literally hundreds of children.

Magpie is a large house at Sheringham in Norfolk. When Mick first went to see it, it was completely empty and the decoration was very drab. As soon as your money started coming in, pots of paint were

Magpie House

purchased and a team of decorators started brightening the place up. Soon it was spick and span and ready to house the equipment that your money was now used to buy. You can see from the shopping list how your money was spent. It bought everything necessary to make the house comfortable and fun.

The Magpie house is next door to a house called Rainbow. This was already a holiday home for handicapped children, but it, too, needed some redecoration and new equipment. So the next project was to spruce up Rainbow. Jenny, Mick and Doug met children from the home when they went to a Christmas party at Sheringham.

With everything possible done on Magpie and Rainbow, your money was used to buy individual pieces of equipment for holiday homes around the country. Among the places that benefited from your

money in this way were houses in Dalvington, Hunstanton, Liverpool, Hastings, Eastern Mordip, Dorchester, Lyme Regis and Ramsgate.

Meanwhile, back in the studio, many people came to marvel at the red line which indicated how much money had been collected and which soon stretched from the Magpie Appeal's special office into the reception area at Teddington—some twenty yards. Michael Crawford, for instance, came to read out some of your letters which told how you had raised money. He said he could imagine the thrill that Jenny, Mick and Doug must have

Rainbow House

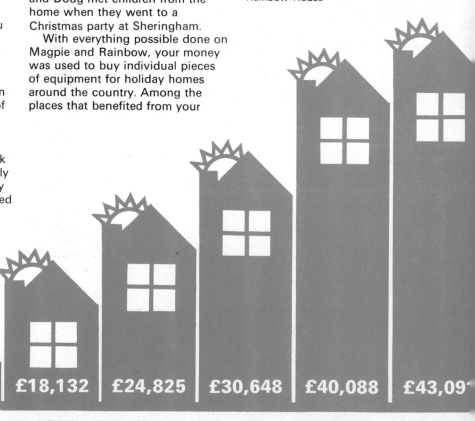

£12,628 £18,132 £24,825 £30,648 £40,088 £43,09

6 Dec   13 Dec 17 Dec 20 Dec 24 Dec 29 Dec 3 Jan

Where they went

got when they opened the first pound's-worth of envelopes. And the fact that this sum had now been multiplied over seventy thousand times was really wonderful.

You used all sorts of ingenious methods to raise money. One of you, for instance, organised a sponsored sandwich-eating session and raised £47.60. Seventy-two of you took part in an ice show at Richmond Rink and made the fantastic sum of over £800. Many of you took part in carol concerts

47,225	£53,808	£57,662	£61,049	£64,109	(closing) £72,160	£82,788
Jan	10 Jan	14 Jan	17 Jan	21 Jan	24 Jan	end Feb

Christmas party at Sheringham

and jumble sales and made Christmas cards and calendars—and gave the money to the Appeal. One of you held a sponsored silence; a group of you even sold daisies for the Appeal. There were also some extraordinarily generous anonymous donations. One person came to Teddington and left £1,000 in five pound notes without giving a name, and someone from Edinburgh posted £600 in cash without saying who they were.

For all the money that was sent for the Appeal, whether it was one pence or a hundred thousand, Magpie thanks you very much indeed.

Money spent on redecorating & equipping 'Magpie'

	£		£
quiet room	183		
dining room	750	playroom	580
extra equipment	842	curtains	975
play equipment	2,292	bathroom	496
extra furniture	604	decorating equipment	2,657
kitchen (approx)	2,500	bedding	700
cottage annexe	348	cleaning equipment	594
table tennis room	157	9 bedrooms	1,964
4 activity rooms	798	laundry	1,898
(including one for music and one for woodwork)		3 recreation rooms	1,104
		nurses room	87
office	182	medical equipment	1,227
2 minibuses	6,133	shower room	71

The Iron Man by Ted Hughes (*Faber & Faber, 35p*)
A powerful science fantasy story about an epic fight between a space monster and the Iron Man.

SPORT ON ICE

Skiing, skating, curling, bobsleigh, ice hockey and tobogganing are all 'winter sports'. There was a time when English people could only take part in these sports if they could afford to travel to countries like Switzerland and Austria where snow and ice can be guaranteed in winter. Nowadays, though, ice rinks and even ski slopes can be artificially produced and winter sports can be done all the year round, even in Britain.

Last year Douglas took part in one winter sport which is becoming very popular with young people—ice hockey, which combines the thrill of speed on ice with the competitiveness of a team game. But first, what about those other winter sports?

The oldest of them all is skiing, which began not as a sport but as a means of transport for Scandinavians who would otherwise have been snowbound for months on end. The most ancient ski that has been discovered is more than 4,500

years old. The old Scandinavian sagas even mention a god of skiing who was called Ullr. Although people have been skiing for such a long time, it didn't become an organised sport until the last century, and it wasn't until 1936 that slalom skiing was recognised as an Olympic sport.

Skating is almost as old as skiing and also originated as a means of transport. The first skates were made from the shank or rib bones of animals such as reindeer and elk. Samuel Pepys saw people skating on the canal in St James's Park, London, and he wrote in his diary in 1662: "It being a great Frost, I did see people sliding with their skeetes, which is a very pretty art." The all-iron skate was invented in 1850 and ice figure skating was first included in the Olympic Games in 1908.

Curling is traditionally a Scottish game, although it probably began in the Netherlands in about 1500, and is now popular in many winter resorts. Curling is rather like bowls-on-ice. Two teams of four people play against each other, each person using two disc-shaped stones. These are propelled across the ice, and a point is scored for each stone that at the end of a round lies nearer the "tee" than an opposing one. Because particles of ice-dust can affect the stone's progress, players are allowed to sweep just in front of the stone and thus adjust its pace and direction. This activity is special to curling and is called "sooping".

Bobsleigh has been an Olympic event since 1924, when the first separate Winter Olympic Games were held at Chamonix. Two or four people sit on a sleigh that hurtles along a set course at speeds that can reach over 80 mph. A winter sport related to bobsleigh is luge tobogganing, which made its Olympic debut in 1964. Luge runs are steeper than bobsleigh runs, with narrower corners; and, unlike the bobsleigh, a luge has no mechanical means of steering.

But what about ice hockey, the fastest man-powered team game in the world? Douglas went along to the Michael Sobell Sports Centre in

London where the country's most successful junior hockey club has its headquarters, to find out more. When the club first started, in January 1974, there was very little money available to buy equipment—and only a handful of the enthusiasts could actually skate. But, undeterred, the club members—aged from seven to sixteen—did odd jobs to make money and eventually raised enough to buy the essential protective clothing and the special skates which cost up to £35 a pair.

The Sobell ice hockey squad train four times a week, practising control of the puck, quick stops, versatile skating and shooting. So they are always ready for a match. This lasts one hour and is usually divided into three 20-minute periods.

There is always lots of action on an ice hockey pitch. Each side has five players plus a goalie, and the whole team can be changed every minute. The team plays in rows of defence men and forwards and usually just one row is changed at a time. The pace of ice hockey is very fast and play is not often stopped. However if a foul takes place, the offending player is sent off the field for a few minutes. The game begins when the referee drops the puck in the centre of the rink between the sticks of two centre-forwards. Players can stop the puck with their hands and bodies and skates, and they can even move it forward by kicking it; but a goal is scored only if the puck has come off a stick.

Playing goalie in ice hockey requires a lot of courage, as Douglas discovered. He was glad for the extra protection that all goalies wear—leg pads, body pads, special gloves and a mask. For when there's nothing between you and a puck hurtling along at up to 60 mph, it's no game!

MASKS

What you need to make the mask: a balloon; newspaper; flour; water; an old bowl; a pin; a felt tipped pen; scissors.

1 Blow up your balloon, mix the flour and water to a thin creamy paste, and cut the newspaper into 6-inch strips.

2 Soak the strips of paper in the paste until they are really soggy.

3 Paste the strips of wet paper on the balloon, smoothing them out to get rid of air bubbles. There should be about four layers of paper on the balloon to make a firm mask. So keep pasting! When you've finished, put the balloon in a warm place to dry. This may take three days.

4 When the balloon is dry, burst it with a pin so that it shrivels away leaving a hard paper shell. Draw a circle all round it . . .

5 and cut along the line to make two halves.

6 Put one half against your face and ask a friend to mark out the eyes and mouth. Cut them out with scissors.

7 Now you can let your imagination rip and decorate the mask. You can paint it in bright colours like Doug's.

8 Or stick on bits of egg boxes for a nose and bulbous eyes, wool for a moustache and twisted newspaper for hair.

9 Or cover it with kitchen foil and stick on bright ribbons.

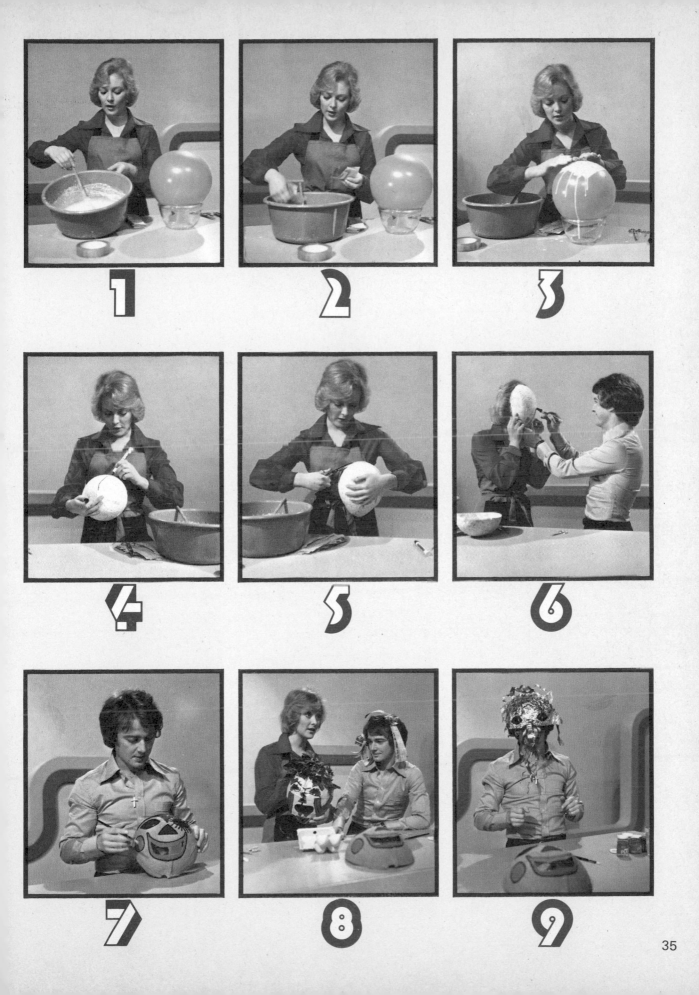

LANDA

In the year AD 43 the Romans, led by Julius Caesar, landed on the Kent coast and began their invasion of Britain. During the following years the Romans, and their way of life, spread throughout the land. By the AD 70's they were reaching the Brigantian hills in the northern counties of England, and within 10 years they had established the first of 17 forts and towns in the area. One of these forts was Vindolanda (the word means white lawns), with a garrison of an infantry battalion numbering 1,000 men. Although these men were Roman citizens, they were not in fact Roman. The soldiers holding the frontier were auxiliaries, drawn from all corners of the Roman Empire: Gaul, Germany, the Netherlands, Spain, Illyria and, in later years, Britain. Only the most senior officers, such as centurions, were Roman, and sometimes not even they were.

Before long the native Brigantian and Votadinian tribesmen of the area were attracted to the fort, lured by the spell of the Pax Romana, and all the rewards of Roman army pay and equipment. Soon a thriving civilian settlement had grown up around the fort of Vindolanda. A township like this was called a "vicus", and was often much larger than the fort itself. Vindolanda had a $3\frac{1}{2}$ acre fort, but a 10 acre vicus. Although it was not officially allowed, many of the troops married local native women. At the end of his 25-year service, many of the auxiliaries would retire to the vicus, often setting up shop to trade to his old mates, and sending his sons into the army. Over the years the distinctions between the races disappeared, and the new breed of Roman–British held the frontier.

In the year AD 120 the Emperor Hadrian decided that the expansionist policies of his predecessors were wrong, and resolved to fix the limits of the 37

Empire. As part of this plan, he ordered the Governor of Britain, Aulus Platorius Nepos, to build a wall across Northern England to mark the border between the warring native tribesmen of the North, the Caledonians, and the Roman Empire. Nepos dispatched men from all three legions that formed the occupying army to the north, and they built a huge wall from Wallsend on the East coast to Bowness on the West, a length of $73\frac{1}{2}$ miles.

On the completion of Hadrian's wall in AD 125 they returned home, and the garrison at Vindolanda, now safely tucked one mile behind the Wall, were moved to Housesteads, a fort actually on the Wall. Vindolanda was deserted until AD 160 when a new fort was built on the site, to house troops stationed on the Wall. Of course a new vicus sprang up, for the fort not only had troops but sat upon the now major East-West trunk road, the Stanegate.

In AD 200 work started on a new fort in the site area, later to house the Cohors IIII Gallorum. In the wake of the fort, extensive civilian building sprang up, including an inn (the *mansio*), bath house, dormitory and married quarters.

Less than 100 years later, in AD 300, the fort and vicus were flattened, and a new fort and vicus were constructed in a new style. In AD 369 new troops from Theodosia replaced the Cohors IIII Gallorum, and extensive repairs and alterations were carried out.

Altogether there were seven forts and "vici" built, one on top of the other, at Vindolanda during the Roman occupation, and archaeological findings from the various periods have helped build up a picture of the rapidly changing community.

Vindolanda is of special interest to archaeologists because of the very earth in which it stands. The heavy

1. *A bird's eye view of the Vindolanda site.*

2. *Part of the wall has been reconstructed in wood—the material used in the later Roman period.*

3. *Douglas watches excavations by pupils from Ashington High School.*

2.

4.

5.

38

clay of the site has no oxygen, and contains a mineral called vivianite; this means that the earth preserves objects. Also, the layers of bracken which the Romans spread on their floors contain chemicals which have further aided the preservation process. In this thick, compressed bracken the archaeologists have found leather articles such as sandals, jewellery, small altars and relics and, above all, wooden writing tablets. Although there is a large amount of Roman writings to be found in museums, it is mostly carved on stone, and is therefore of a formal nature. The writing found on the wooden writing tablets is less formal; it records orders to detachments on the Wall, bills to merchants, letters to the troops, and gives a unique insight to the times.

The wooden writing tablets found compressed in the crushed bracken floor start to decay within 10 minutes of reaching the air, so it is necessary to get them out quickly. They are chopped out, rather like pieces of turf, soaked in water to prevent drying, and then carefully peeled apart under controlled conditions in the laboratory.

At Vindolanda life-sized replicas of various buildings have been constructed so that the problems that faced the Roman builders and the methods they employed to overcome them can be studied. For example, in constructing a 15 feet section of the wall, it has been found that at least 20 men were needed to keep one mason busy, supplying him with the necessary 80 gallons of water, the tons of limestone and coal used to make mortar, the 40 pine poles for scaffolding, not to mention the tons of stone itself.

Another interesting aspect of the Vindolanda project is that children are allowed on the dig as part of their normal school curriculum. Douglas visited a group of children from Ashington High School who were spending one week at the site, learning about digging techniques and the preparation and classification of finds. They were finding the course hard work, physically as well as intellectually, but very rewarding, especially when they actually found something in the earth.

There are not many sites like Vindolanda which allow people under the age of sixteen to help excavate. There is an organization, though, called Young Rescue (New Hall, Cambridge CB3 0DF), which you can join. For the 75 pence membership fee you get a badge and a card and, four times a year, the Young Rescue Newsletter. This tells you about sites throughout the country which might allow you to dig. It also gives you news of activities in local branches which might be close to you.

4. *A reconstructed stone look-out post on the wall.*

5. *Remains of the military bath house.*

39

Jenny as Jennie

Last year, you may have watched the television series 'Jennie, Lady Randolph Churchill', in which the American actress Lee Remick played the title role of Winston Churchill's mother. Jennie was herself an American who came to England in the 1870s and met Lord Randolph Churchill, son of the seventh Duke of Marlborough. They married in 1874 and had two sons, the elder of whom became Sir Winston. On Magpie, Jenny showed you a few of the eighty costumes specially created for the television series, each one accurate to the year in which Jennie would have worn it.

One of the dresses worn by Lee Remick in Jennie, *drawn by Jane Robinson who designed the whole of Lee Remick's wardrobe.*

An 1874 evening dress made of eau de nil organza with embroidered organza flowers and eau de nil and pale yellow on the bodice and skirt.

The dress that Jennie wore at the ball on board HMS Ariadne at which she met Lord Randolph for the first time. It is made of white spotted organza with organza flowers in pink and white and matching detail on the bodice and skirt, and is worn over a half-crinoline.

An outfit designed to make Jennie look fashionable while expecting Winston. The embroidered mauve velvet *pardessus* has a Persian lamb collar, hem and cuffs, while the dark brown moire skirt is trimmed with velvet ribbon and lampshade tassels. The hat and muff are also made of velvet and Persian lamb.

In 1900, when she married George Cornwallis-West—Lord Randolph died in 1895—Jennie started wearing a kimono instead of a teagown, thereby setting a fashion. This one is made of black silk crepe de chine.

An afternoon dress which Jennie would have worn in 1907, made of chiffon and satin with a lace collar forming part of the bodice.

THE FORGING OF A NATION!

IT HAPPENS EVERY FOURTH OF JULY. AT HOME OR ABROAD, CITIZENS OF THE UNITED STATES OF AMERICA GO GLEEFULLY WILD, CELEBRATING IN TRUE AMERICAN STYLE THE ANNIVERSARY OF THE DECLARATION OF INDEPENDENCE—THE BOLD, DARING DECLARATION OF 1776 THAT WAS TO PLUNGE THEIR COUNTRY INTO SEVEN YEARS OF BITTER WARFARE!

AND YET, BUT FOR A COMBINATION OF CIRCUMSTANCES, THESE SAME UNITED STATES OF AMERICA MIGHT STILL HAVE BEEN IN NOMINAL ALLEGIANCE TO THE QUEEN... A DOMINION, LIKE CANADA, PERHAPS—STILL WITHIN THE BRITISH COMMONWEALTH! IT ALL BEGAN IN THE 1760'S—IN AN ATMOSPHERE OF SMOULDERING DISCONTENT...

YEARS OF WAR IN EUROPE HAD BROUGHT CHAOS TO THE BRITISH ECONOMY. THE GOVERNMENT NEEDED MONEY... WHICH MEANT TAXATION... AND THE BRUNT FELL ON THE THIRTEEN COLONIES OF NORTH AMERICA...

AIN'T RIGHT WE SHOULD HAVE TO PAY!

WE'RE GETTIN' EVEN MORE TO FORK OUT! SOME DURNED THING CALLED A STAMP TAX! EVERY DOCUMENT HAS TO CARRY A DUTY—FROM SIX CENTS, RIGHT UP TO FIFTY DOLLARS!

WAY I SEE IT—IF THEY WANT THEIR MONEY, THEY BETTER COME AN' TAKE IT!

POINT-BLANK REFUSAL OVER THE THE HATED STAMP TAX SHOOK PARLIAMENT IN DISTANT WESTMINSTER—SO THEY HASTILY REPEALED IT!

GENTLEMEN! WE CAN PACIFY THESE COLONISTS... BUT IMPOSE OTHER, DIFFERENT TAXES!

YES. BUT THEY CHALLENGE THE MONARCHY'S AUTHORITY! WE MUST SHOW THAT WE'RE NOT A PACK OF WEAK-WILLED FOOLS!

BUT FOOLS THEY WERE! AND NEW MEASURES, PASSED IN THE INFAMOUS TOWNSEND ACT, ONLY INCREASED THE COLONIST'S FURY...

DANG ME! WE'VE GOT TO FEED AN' QUARTER THESE REDCOATS... BY LAW!

THE BRITISH ARE MILKING US DRY! THEY'LL TAKE EVERY CENT WE EARN IF WE LET 'EM!

FEELING RAN HIGH, AND INEVITABLY, RIOTS BROKE OUT...

TELL KING GEORGE TO KEEP YOU!

PACK UP AND GO! WE DON'T WANT YOU HERE!

DISPERSE, CONFOUND YOU, OR MY MEN WILL FIRE!

AND THEN IT HAPPENED! THE ACTION OF A HOTHEAD!

THEY'VE ASKED FOR IT, LADS! GIVE THEM A VOLLEY!

INFURIATED, THE BRITISH PUT MASSACHUSETTS UNDER MILITARY CONTROL! IN SEPTEMBER 1774, REPRESENTATIVES OF THE COLONISTS MET IN PHILADELPHIA TO FORM THE FIRST CONTINENTAL CONGRESS...

AS ILL-FEELING AND HATRED BLOSSOMED, THE BRITISH GOVERNMENT DECIDED TO THINK AGAIN... BUT IT WAS TOO LATE!

WE MUST DRAW UP A DECLARATION OF RIGHTS—TO PRESENT TO OUR COLONISTS, TO THE CANADIANS, TO THE BRITISH PEOPLE, AND TO THE KING!

I SECOND THAT! WE HAVE RIGHT ON OUR SIDE! TAXATION WITHOUT REPRESENTATION IS TYRANNY!

ON DECEMBER 16, 1773, YOUNG BOSTONIANS, DISGUISED AS INDIANS, RAIDED A BRITISH SHIP IN BOSTON HARBOUR AND THREW OVERBOARD 340 CHESTS OF TEA — TAXED AT THREE PENCE PER POUND...!

THE BRITISH GOVERNOR WAS OUTRAGED!

YOU MEAN TO TELL ME THESE MINUTE-MEN HAVE SET UP A MUNITIONS STORE? AT CONCORD? THEY'LL REGRET THIS, BY GLORY!

OPEN REVOLT HAD BEGUN! THE FOLLOWING YEAR, A COMMITTEE OF SAFETY AT CAMBRIDGE, MASSACHUSETTS, ORDERED A MILITARY FORCE OF 2000 MEN TO BE FORMED...

THIS'LL SHOW THE BRITISH WE MEAN BUSINESS! OUR MEN MAY BE ROUGH AN' READY, BUT THEY'LL FIGHT!

YEP, FARMERS, SHOPKEEPERS AN' MECHANICS —BUT THEY'LL BE READY TO BE SOLDIERS AT A MINUTE'S NOTICE!

43

INSTANTLY, A BRITISH FORCE WAS DESPATCHED TO SEIZE THE ARMOURY... BUT THE MINUTE-MEN WERE CALLED UP! THE TWO FORCES MET AT LEXINGTON...

USED TO AN ENEMY WHICH STOOD AND EXCHANGED FIRE FOR FIRE, THE BRITISH HADN'T A CHANCE! FIRING FROM COVER, AND IN BROKEN FORMATION, THE COLONISTS WREAKED ABSOLUTE HAVOC!

LOOK AT 'EM COME! LIKE THEY WAS ON PARADE!

FIGHTIN' BY A BOOK O' RULES! I HOPE THEY DON'T THINK WE'RE GONNA BE SO CRAZY!

THIS ISN'T FAIR FIGHTING! THEY'RE BREAKING ALL THE RULES OF WAR!

STAND FIRM, DAMN YOU! STAND FIRM!

WE'VE BEATEN 'EM, BY HICKORY!

YAAAYY! WE'VE GOT THE REDCOATS ON THE RUN!

THE NEWS OF THE AMAZING VICTORY RACED THROUGH THE COLONIES! IN VERMONT, THE 'GREEN MOUNTAIN BOYS' ROSE AND STORMED FORT TICONDEROGA, CAPTURING IT!

IT WAS JUNE 1775. A MEETING OF CONGRESS GAVE COMMAND OF THE CONTINENTAL ARMY OF AMERICA TO THEIR MOST PROMISING GENERAL — GEORGE WASHINGTON...

I MOVE THAT THESE UNITED STATES ARE FREE AND INDEPENDENT! THAT ALL POLITICAL CONNECTION BETWEEN THEM AND GREAT BRITAIN IS, AND OUGHT TO BE TOTALLY DISSOLVED!

RAGGED... SHORT OF POWDER AND SHOT... LOW ON DISCIPLINE! BUT BY THE STARS, LOOK AT THE FERVOUR OF THEM! WITH MEN LIKE THESE, WE'LL WIN!

THE DIE WAS CAST. ON JUNE 7, 1776, RICHARD LEE, SPOKESMAN FOR VIRGINIA, MADE A HISTORIC RECOMMENDATION TO CONGRESS...

I SECOND THAT RESOLUTION!

AGAINST OPPOSITION, JOHN AND LEE ADAMS FORCED THE MOTION THROUGH. ON JULY 4, 1776, THE RESOLUTION WAS ADOPTED! THE GREAT AMERICAN REVOLUTION HAD OFFICIALLY BEGUN!

WE'VE PROVOKED A CRISIS, BENJAMIN! WHATEVER HAPPENS NOW, WE MUST ALL HANG TOGETHER!

IF NOT, HANCOCK, WE SHALL ALL HANG SEPARATELY!

EXCITEMENT RAN AT FEVER PITCH! WASHINGTON'S FORCES, IN CONTROL OF BOSTON SINCE THE SPRING, FACED THE RETURN OF GENERAL HOWE WITH A FORCE OF 25,000 BRITISH AND HESSIAN MERCENARY ALLIES!

NOW WE'LL SEE HOW THE REBELS STAND UP TO SHOT AND SHELL!

MARK MY WORDS — THEY'VE BEEN LUCKY SO FAR! THEY'LL CRACK SOON ENOUGH BEFORE A TRAINED ARMY!

AND WASHINGTON WITHDREW, RETREATING TO NEWARK, NEW JERSEY, WITH THE BRITISH AT HIS HEELS!

CONFOUND THESE COLONIAL BLACKGUARDS! THEIR REARGUARD AMBUSHES US AT EVERY STEP!

HOLD 'EM OFF, BOYS! THEY MUSTN'T GET AT THE MAIN FORCE!

FOR A WHILE, THE AMERICAN CAUSE WAS IN TROUBLE! A PERSONALITY CLASH BETWEEN WASHINGTON AND GENERAL CHARLES LEE THREATENED TO SPLIT THE CONTINENTAL ARMY!

LEE REFUSES TO BRING HIS MEN TO OUR AID! WE MUST FALL BACK TO PHILADELPHIA!

AWAY ON THE HUDSON, LEE WAS CAPTURED. BUT HIS FORCE ESCAPED TO JOIN WASHINGTON—AND ON CHRISTMAS NIGHT, 1776, THE AMERICANS TOOK 1,000 HESSIANS PRISONER AT THE BATTLE OF TRENTON!

I MUST REMEMBER TO WRITE AN' THANK KING GEORGE FOR ALL THESE NEW GUNS AN' EQUIPMENT!

SURE! WRAP A NOTE ROUND A BULLET AN' FIRE IT AT HIM!

EVER-CHANGING, THE FORTUNE OF WAR BROUGHT REVERSAL IN THE WAKE OF VICTORY. WASHINGTON ROUTED THREE BRITISH REGIMENTS, BUT A FORCE UNDER GENERAL HOWE, LANDING AT CHESAPEAKE BAY, DEFEATED HIM ON THE BRANDYWINE RIVER!

AN ATTEMPT TO REGROUP AT PHILADELPHIA FAILED, AND ONCE MORE WASHINGTON HAD TO RETREAT. HIS ARMY WINTERED AT VALLEY FORGE... AN ARMY IN PITIABLE CONDITION!

POOR DEVILS! AND YET I MUST ASK THEM FOR MORE STRENGTH... MORE EFFORT!

THEIR SHOES ARE WORN OUT, SIR! YOU CAN SEE THE BLOOD OF THEIR FEET ON THE SNOW!

SPRING BROUGHT NEW HOPE! THE BRITISH MADE ONE OF THEIR NOTORIOUS BLUNDERS, DIVIDING THEIR ARMIES INSTEAD OF MASSING FOR A COMBINED ASSAULT. CAUGHT ALONE AT SARATOGA, GENERAL BURGOYNE AND HIS FORCE SURRENDERED!

THIS IS THE FIRST DECISIVE VICTORY WE'VE WON, GENERAL!

LET US HOPE IT WILL BE THE FIRST OF MANY...!

NEWS OF THE TRIUMPH BROUGHT ASSISTANCE FROM FRANCE—LONG AN ENEMY OF THE BRITISH. A FLEET OF WARSHIPS SAILED FOR THE NEW WORLD...

WHAT'S THE MATTER WITH OUR FRIGATES? CAN'T THEY PROTECT US FROM CAPTURE BY THESE ROGUES?

THEY CAN'T SAIL FAST ENOUGH TO CATCH US, MISTER—AN' THAT'S THE TRUTH!

MEANWHILE, THE AMERICAN NAVY—A HOTCH-POTCH OF HASTILY-BUILT WARSHIPS AND CONVERTED MERCHANTMEN, BACKED BY SWIFT AND DARING PRIVATEERS—HARRASSED BRITISH COMMERCE...

AMERICANS THRILLED TO THE EXPLOITS OF THEIR SCOTTISH CAPTAIN, JOHN PAUL JONES—SO AUDACIOUS THAT HE ACTUALLY ATTACKED SHIPPING IN THE BRITISH PORT OF WHITEHAVEN, AND CAPTURED HMS DRAKE ..!

ON THE AMERICAN CONTINENT, THE BRITISH, DRIVEN MAD BY THE STUBBORN RESISTANCE OF THEIR ENEMY, STRUCK SOUTH, HOPING TO DRAW WASHINGTON AWAY FROM NEW YORK. AT CHARLESTON, SOUTH CAROLINA, GENERAL CORNWALLIS DEFEATED AN AMERICAN ARMY ..!

GENTLEMEN, WE HAVE THE MEASURE OF THESE REBELS, AT LAST! ONE OF THEIR LEADERS, BENEDICT ARNOLD, HAS COME OVER TO US...

HE ACTUALLY HANDED OVER THE FORT AT WEST POINT, SIR. PERHAPS WASHINGTON IS LOSING HIS GRIP OVER HIS OFFICERS...

THERE WAS NO SUCH LUCK FOR THE BRITISH! IN ONE FURIOUS BURST, OF DETERMINATION, A NEW AMERICAN ARMY UNDER GENERAL NATHANIEL GREENE FELL LIKE A THUNDERBOLT ON THE ALLIED TROOPS AT COWPENS, SOUTH CAROLINA...

APPALLED, CORNWALLIS FELL BACK TO YORKTOWN, VIRGINIA, THERE TO FIND HIMSELF SURROUNDED!

WE MUST EVACUATE, SIR... BY SEA!

ARE YOU MAD, MAN? WITH THE FRENCH FLEET WAITING FOR US! THERE IS ONLY ONE COURSE LEFT...

WE MUST SURRENDER!

OCTOBER 19, 1781. FIVE YEARS AND THREE MONTHS AFTER THE AMERICAN DECLARATION OF INDEPENDENCE. APART FROM THE ODD SKIRMISH THAT WAS TO GO ON FOR ANOTHER YEAR OR SO, THE GREAT AMERICAN REVOLUTION WAS OVER...!

IN NOVEMBER 1782, THE TREATY OF PEACE WAS DRAWN UP. IN 1783, IT HAD BECOME FINAL. A NEW FLAG WAS RECOGNISED BY A DEJECTED BRITISH GOVERNMENT—AND A NEW NATION WAS BORN!

LONG LIVE AMERICA!

LONG LIVE THE UNITED STATES!

LONG LIVE LIBERTY!

PATENTS

Regd. trade mark Patents pending

One of the qualities that distinguishes man from other animals is his inventiveness. From the time that he first started making tools out of stone and flint, he has gone on inventing machines and gadgets which might be useful to him. Sometimes he's got rather carried away with himself.

The trouble is that it's difficult for the amateur in a technological age to invent a machine that is superior to one already on the market. The result is that many wierd and wonderful ideas have remained just that—no one has ever been such a fool as to invest good money in making gadgets that no one would buy.

In the patents office in London there is ample evidence of man's well-intentioned but useless inventiveness for, since 1624, under the Law of Monopolies, it has been possible to take out letters of patent for your idea—provided it is really original—and in that way stop anyone else pinching it. Thousands of jealous inventors, thinking they were on to a good thing, have done this.

Take this variation on the bike: 'Improved Sunshade, Umbrella or Sail for Cyclists. Ideal for use in all weathers and on the sea!' Oh yes? But if you're travelling along, the rain will soak your front; it won't obligingly hit the top of the umbrella. And if you're at sea on your bike—well, you really would be at sea.

How about this tandem for courting couples. If you want to be in the constant gaze of your beloved, then it's a great idea. On the other hand, if someone is riding backwards directly in front of you, how can you see where you're going? And if you have to steer through your partner's back wheel, the bike is hardly going to be stable. No, this tandem would bring love to a premature end, not prolong it.

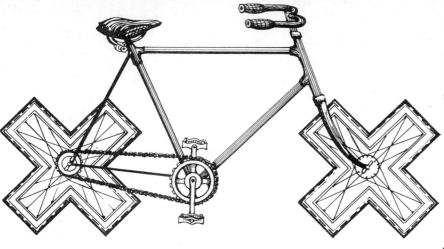

A final bike invention—one for going up and down steps. Seems a good idea, doesn't it? But only if all steps were the same size. And anyway, would it really catch on?

How about the Pedespeed, the idea for which was patented in 1870. It consists of two wheels, each with a wooden platform for a foot and straps which attach the wheels to the legs. Put them on and you can do everything that you could do on an iceskate, plus more because you can use the pedespeed on any type of surface, not just ice. In the words of the hopeful inventor: "The Pedespeed affords a delightful, healthful and graceful pastime at all seasons of the year." Sounds all right. But wait a minute—how do you stop, short of crashing into a tree? And imagine the muscle-power required to prevent yourself doing the splits!

Still on the subject of transport, look at the Natural Flying-Machine. The inventor, remembering tales about eagles picking up babies, reckoned that ten eagles would be enough to fly a full-grown man through the air. He wrote in 1865: "In the accompanying drawing I have indicated how the eagles, by means of jackets fixed round their bodies, could be attached to a circular framework of hollow tubes which could carry aloft a metal basket large enough to hold a man, thus forming a natural flying machine." Well, where's the catch in that?

49

Victorian people didn't only patent inventions for use outside; they thought up all sorts of ideas for machines that might be handy about the house, too.

The Velocipede Shower-Bath for instance, invented in 1897. This is a combined keep-fit and washing machine. You keep in trim by pedalling and in so doing rotate a pump which forces water from a tank. The harder you pedal, the fitter you become and the more luxuriantly the water flows.

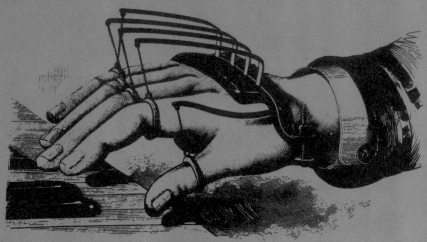

This is Atkin's Finger Supporting Device, patented in 1881 to help piano-players maintain the correct horizontal finger position as far as the second joint. Looks a bit painful...and anyway, if you need such a machine, should you be playing the piano?

You might do better to take up one of these instruments— the cello-piano or the viola-piano, both patented in 1893. By using the piano keyboard you obtain an accuracy of note that many people find difficult if they are using their left hand on the stringed instrument itself. At the same time you achieve the beauty of tone that belongs to the cello or viola.

Here's a gadget you might try out on your dad to stop him snoring—a kind of harness which keeps his mouth tight shut. One can imagine it would do its job—but by keeping dad awake all night.

POYET

When the Victorians took out patents, they were perfectly serious about their inventions—they hoped they would be made up as genuinely useful articles.

A more modern inventor, Frenchman Jacques Carelman, is someone who has patented all his inventions but hardly expects them to be manufactured. Nevertheless, some of them do have a bizarrely practical ring about them.

Here are a few.

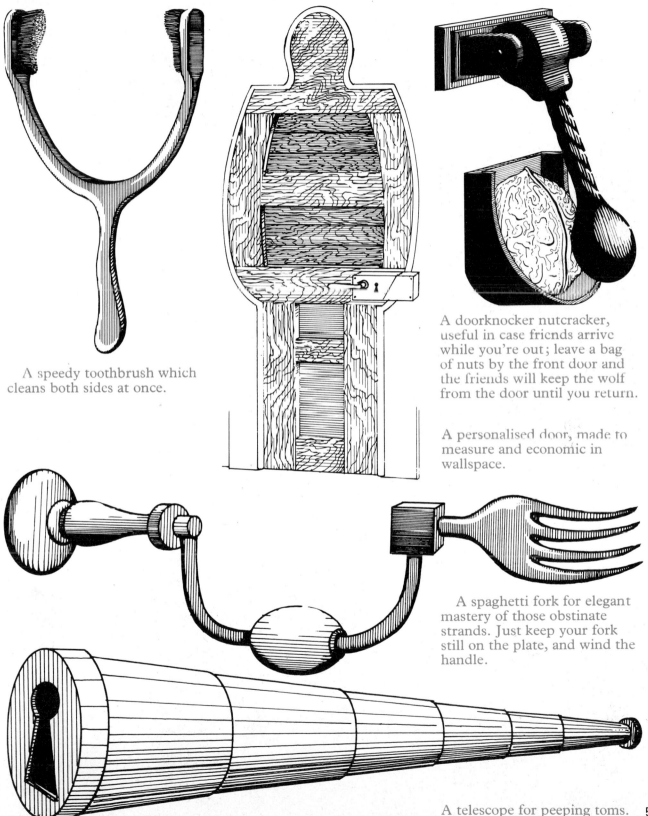

A speedy toothbrush which cleans both sides at once.

A doorknocker nutcracker, useful in case friends arrive while you're out; leave a bag of nuts by the front door and the friends will keep the wolf from the door until you return.

A personalised door, made to measure and economic in wallspace.

A spaghetti fork for elegant mastery of those obstinate strands. Just keep your fork still on the plate, and wind the handle.

A telescope for peeping toms. 51

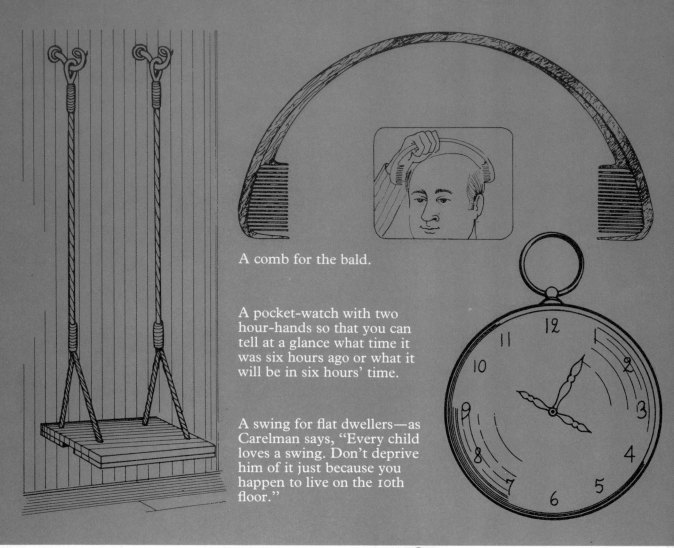

A comb for the bald.

A pocket-watch with two hour-hands so that you can tell at a glance what time it was six hours ago or what it will be in six hours' time.

A swing for flat dwellers—as Carelman says, "Every child loves a swing. Don't deprive him of it just because you happen to live on the 10th floor."

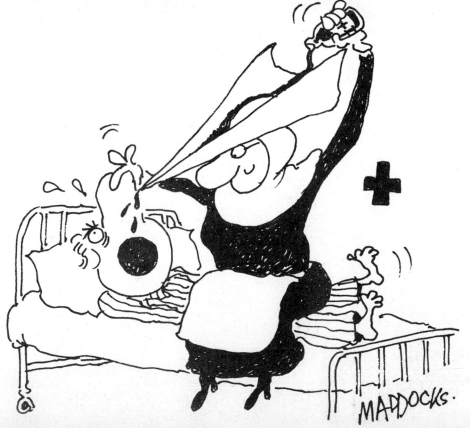

CRACK THE CODE—
Win a Prize.

The poem below, by an English poet, is printed in code. We'd like you to crack the code then find out its title and who wrote it. Send just the title and name of the poet, together with your own name and address, on a postcard, to:

Code Competition,
Magpie,
Thames Television,
Teddington Lock,
Middlesex.

The closing date for entries is 31 January 1976. The first twenty-five correct answers picked out of a hat will win book tokens worth £1.

FI KBMUXU TFI KVMG QETF KVYYCIJ FMZJU:

KBYUI TY TFI USZ EZ BYZIBO BMZJU,

VEZGIJ QETF TFI MNSVI QYVBJ, FI UTMZJU.

TFI QVEZCBIJ UIM LIZIMTF FEA KVMQBU;

FI QMTKFIU HVYA FEU AYSZTMEZ QMBBU,

MZJ BECI M TFSZJIVLYBT FI HMBBU.

Last Annual's Code Decoded

We thought that last year's code was practically impossible. You didn't only have to crack the code —you also had to solve the riddle that the code contained. Yet hundreds and hundreds of you sent in postcards with the correct answer which was, simply: MAN. The riddle was the one that the Sphinx asked King Oedipus: "What living thing walks on four legs in the morning, on two legs in the afternoon, and on three legs in the evening?"

Congratulations to all who solved the riddle, particularly to the twenty-five entrants whose answers were picked from a hat and won £1 book tokens: Esme Hattem, Kathryn Duncan, Veronica Fenlon, J. Forestal, Lucy McCrickard, Ann Seymour, Rosemary Farrow, Janice Davies, Christine Mansfield, Mark Mawson, Adrian Wood, Hilary Matchett, Sarah Carden, Antoinette Bland, Martin Rolfe, Alexander Cobbold, Tina Scillitoe, Clive Freedman, Sally Meredith, Karen Matthews, Judith Hackett, Tracy Hasted, Helen Turpin, Judith Ainsworth and Fiona Gibson.

Know Your Onions

Douglas is standing with a man wearing a French beret. They are both surrounded by onions and both are stringing them onto rushes. Doug has clearly never done this before; his companion is obviously an expert. Doug introduces his friend: "This is Albert Daridon. He is one of the few onion johnnies still selling onions in this country – one of 64 in fact. How am I doing Albert?"

"Not very well – you'll have to do better than that if you want to sell onions to my customers."

Now Douglas and Albert are riding along a street with strings of onions straddling their handlebars. They visit a lady called Mrs Burn who buys two strings at a pound each; Albert explains she is one of his best customers and he's been selling to her for thirty years. Then the two of them visit the Café Royal restaurant and after some haggling sell onions to the chef at the back door.

Now Douglas is on his own, trying to sell onions to housewives in Wimbledon. He's having no luck – people want Albert's onions, not Doug's. We see him being rejected by one lady and coming out of several front gates looking miserable. Albert, on the other hand, is rapidly getting rid of all the onions hanging on his bike.

Douglas and Albert meet; Albert's bike is empty, Douglas's full. They ride off together down the street.

That, briefly, was the onion-selling story which you saw last year on Magpie. It lasted 7 minutes 10 seconds. Yet it had taken twelve people one whole day to film, another morning to 'dub' the commentary and another to cut it down to the required few minutes.

It all started at the little house beside a garage in Surbiton where Albert and his wife and two cousins live from August until March each year, selling French onions. (The rest of the year they live in the small French village of Roskoff near the sea where they are farmers.) Albert knew to expect Magpie that day because he'd already been visited by researcher Helen Dickinson. Everyone was due to be there at 9.30. It was a bitterly cold, but bright day. The film crew arrived, and while waiting for the props men to come with Douglas's bike, Albert was fitted up with a radio microphone which would record what he said, and a welcome flask of coffee was produced.

Meanwhile, where was Douglas? Everyone stood around blowing on their hands and stamping their feet. "You'll get sunstroke", quipped one passer-by.

He turned up a few minutes later, held up on his way back from Edinburgh by a bomb scare at Heathrow. He quickly put on his microphone, said hallo to Albert then the two of them were ready for filming.

Audrey, the director, said "Turn over sound".

Eric on sound: "Running".

"Magpie Onion Selling, Scene One Take One", said Malcolm, working the clapper board.

"Action", said Audrey.

The film was under way, with shots of Doug and Albert loading up their bicycles. All was going well until a garage mechanic came "into shot". "Cut", was Audrey's

immediate reaction, and Malcolm chalked up "Take 2".

Now what was needed was a shot of Doug and Albert riding down the road. So the camera was loaded into the van and, when there was a break in the traffic, it set out down the busy street with Doug and Albert riding behind for a "tracking" shot. In that way, you were able to see their front views on the television. The idea was that they should ride round the block. After a few minutes, Douglas returned — but where was the van and Albert? They soon turned up and all was well except that Audrey noticed Douglas had an onion in his pocket. "Oh dear", she said, "Now he'll have to keep that there all day or people will notice he hasn't got it."

The tracking shot completed, it was time to drive to Wimbledon where most of Albert's customers live. Albert would usually bicycle the six miles, but today he and his bike rode in the props van.

Before visiting their first customer, Mrs Burn, Doug and Albert had to be filmed arriving on their bikes — it wouldn't be revealed on television, of course, that they had driven there.

Mrs Burn had already been visited the week before by Helen Dickinson, so she was expecting Magpie, although perhaps not quite so many people. Everyone crowded into her tiny courtyard while Mrs Burn obediently bought her onions — even though, as she pointed out, she already had several strings in her garage, bought last week on Albert's monthly visit.

By now everyone was very cold and hungry, so the whole group walked up the road to the Café Royal restaurant, whose chef had been asked to have lunch ready. Later, of course, he was going to be filmed buying Albert's onions.

The first course, appropriately, was French Onion Soup — made of the onions that Albert had delivered on his last regular visit. Over lunch, Albert talked about himself and his work.

French onion sellers, he said, had been coming to England since 1870. He himself first started coming over with his father when he was eleven years old. There were then about 200 French onion sellers working in London and about 2,000 throughout England. Now that number has dwindled to just ten in London and 64 in the whole country. Albert has two sons, but neither intend following in their father's footsteps; one is a policeman and one a painter. Onion selling is no longer as lucrative as it once was because of the falling rate of English money against the franc. Still, Albert sells between 50 and 60 tons of onions a year and at 50 pence a small string of 12 onions — or £1 for larger, double ones, he reckons it's worth his while continuing — and in any case, selling onions in England is a way of life for him, not just a way of making a living.

Albert can carry about 50 bunches of onions on his bike and he has usually sold out by the end of the day. He also owns a van and sometimes, especially when he's going beyond his usual beat of Wimbledon, he carries his onions in that. He finds, though, that his customers prefer to see him on a bicycle — it's all part of the tradition — so he sells more onions if he travels that way.

In France, onions are sold loose. In England, customers expect their French onions to be elegantly strung. At weekends, Albert often has to travel to Weybridge in order to pick the bulrushes used for onion-stringing.

French onions, many people think, are tastier than home-grown ones. They are pinkish inside and cut like butter. If strung in a cool place, they keep quite a long time. To his compatriots, Albert speaks 'patois' but he spoke English with a delightful French accent when talking to Magpie.

Lunch over, it was time to film Doug and Albert arriving at the back door of the Café Royal and bartering with the chef — who entered into the spirit. This done, it was back into the vans and off to sell at one or two houses that didn't know Magpie was arriving. First, though, Douglas got accosted by a lady who didn't realise that he was not a real onion seller. Doug played his part to perfection and handed over a string. Albert was very impressed.

Now, the story as you were going to see it on television was that Douglas couldn't sell his onions, so Doug was just filmed coming out of all the gates in Somerset Road looking dejected having sold no onions. One lady was asked to slam her window in Douglas's face. But Douglas was so persuasive that she eventually said she would buy some onions! That sequence had to be filmed again and this time the lady played her part correctly.

55

Next, to show that Albert was selling all his onions, he was filmed simply taking one string after another off his bicycle and walking out of the view of the camera. In this way the impression of hectic selling was given. Of course, Albert *could* have sold his onions in the day – but with all the filming there was hardly time for him actually to do so. And the chances are that Douglas wouldn't *really* make a very good onion-seller, even though he had a bit of beginner's luck on this day.

There was just enough light to film Doug and Albert riding off down the street together (the end of the film as you saw it), before everyone returned to the Surbiton loft above the garage where Albert and his cousins store their onions and string them. It took some while to get everyone up the precarious ladder to the loft, which measured only about 18 feet square. Soon the whole of the loft was filled with people and cameras and lights and sound booms; television had taken over. There was just a small area for Doug to be filmed talking to Albert, while the two cousins silently and rhythmically got on with their

stringing. It took them each about two minutes to make up a bunch of twelve, attaching the onion stalks to the bulrushes with lengths of raffia. The russet-coloured stack of onions and piles of green rushes made an attractive setting. But, in seven minutes, there wasn't time to show you much of it.

This was going to be the opening of the film on television, so Douglas and Albert had to be careful to use the correct tense – talking about what they were *going* to do, not what they *had* done. They forgot once, and once Douglas forgot to ask Albert an important question, so there were three 'takes' for that scene.

At last, the day was almost over. All that was needed was two minutes silence while Eric recorded 'atmosphere' noise – authentic sounds that you would hear as background. During the two minutes, Douglas closed his eyes; as usual, filming a story for Magpie had been great fun, but it had also been exhausting. He was looking forward to going home and having a good supper of steak and fried onions – made from the onions that he didn't sell, of course!

The Kingdom Under the Sea folk tales retold by Joan Aiken (illustrated by Jan Pienkowski) (*Puffin, 50p*)
A collection of beautiful stories from Eastern Europe, first told a hundred years ago. They are full of witches, dragons, princesses and magic, as well as simple folk like fishermen and poor girls, and they tell of people's wisdom and wickednesses which are the same today as they were a century ago.

"I'VE WARNED YOU BEFORE ABOUT WEARING TIGHTS!"

MADDOCKS' MIRTH

BORN UNDER AQUARIUS —?
WELL IT MAKES A CHANGE
FROM THE GOOSEBERRY BUSH!

MY DAD ALWAYS SAYS, YOU CAN'T GET THE CRAFTSMEN THESE DAYS LIKE YOU USED TO!

What's an ADVENTURE PLAYGROUND?

by John Birtwhistle

When I think of playgrounds, I think of two very different kinds. First I think of the asphalt yard at my school, marked out with white lines for team games, with a metal climbing frame in one corner. But then I think of the real playgrounds, the places I have found for myself and really enjoyed playing in.

All along the road to my school there was a brook that someone told me joined up in the end with the River Thames. It had trees and bushes on its banks, and you could cross it by foot bridges, or sometimes by a plank or pipe; and we put stepping stones in it so you could cross it that way too. At one place, it went underground through a slimy green tunnel.

This brook was strictly out of bounds. Even though we knew that somewhere it gave into the Thames, our parents and teachers said it was just a dirty ditch. We were told to hurry past it and get to school on time, and then hurry past it and get home safely. But often we would be trying to dam it up, or balancing along one of the pipes that crossed it, or getting a shoeful of muddy water. Once, a boy even tried to go down the tunnel and come out with the stream the other end.

Now, if you can think of somewhere like that where you have had a good time, you already have a good idea of what kind of playground it is that is called an Adventure Playground.

My first Adventure Playground was near where I lived in London. From the outside it looked just like a lot of other building sites, fenced off with corrugated iron. Except that the fence was covered all over with paintings in hundreds of colours. Paintings of faces and names and football slogans, and a big sign which said "WELCOME TO THE ADVENTURE: every day from 4 to 8 o'clock, and all day Saturdays".

Most people, when they come for the first time, wait a bit at the entrance, looking in and wondering what to make of it all. At first it seems like noisy chaos. You can see mothers hurrying their kids past the entrance just as they did past my brook. It's no use coming to an Adventure Playground in your best clothes.

An Adventure Playground is a patch of land, parts of it piled up into little hills, and if you are lucky there will also be woods and water. There is often a huge tower built on one of the hills. It will be made of logs or railway sleepers, and have ladders running up to it and ropes and a slide running down from it. Then at a lower level, there are huts and piles of wood from which you can make your own huts. Then there are things like a sand pit for the smaller kids. And under everything there is a system of tunnels through the hills of earth.

Don't get the idea, though, that the main thing about an Adventure Playground is the way it is built. What's important is that it's a place to go and play in just as you want. Or if you don't feel like playing at all, you can light a fire and stand around it talking, perhaps roasting potatoes in the embers, and watch the changing colours of metals burning in the fire. This is especially good in winter.

That is the outside part of it. Then, most Adventure Playgrounds have a hut. Ours was an old garage, and it had a table-tennis table with forms around it, a radio, carpentry tools, painting things and so on.

An Adventure Playground has nothing to do with schools, or the kinds of playgrounds you get in schools. You don't have to do anything you don't want to do. If you have an idea — say you have the idea of making a swing out of rope and a tyre, then you just go off and scrounge the materials and build it. In the same way, if you just want to talk to your friends, you just stand around and talk, and no one will blow a whistle and tell you that you ought to be doing something else.

Who goes to an Adventure Playground? Anybody can join in, girls as well as boys, young children as well as school-leavers. Girls are just as good with hammers and saws as boys are, and boys are just as good at weaving, and in the Adventure Playground everybody can try their hands at anything. There is usually a gang of people who come nearly every evening, but just as important are those who wander in once in a while.

There are also a couple of adults there, and I used to be one of these myself in the playground I've told you about. Our job was to find materials of all kinds, and generally look after the place. Fortunately, we didn't

being closed. Footpaths are being blocked and old trees felled, roads are more dangerous than they used to be. So, wherever you live, if there is no Adventure Playground near enough to you, how could you set about making one?

You will have talked about it with your friends and some of them will want to help. You will have to get a lot of help from adults —like parents, teachers and town councillors — but the main thing is your group of friends. It is going to be your playground, and if you are well enough organised you can get your own way.

have to keep telling people what to do: the playground belongs to the children who use it, and they can use it as they wish. Myself, I used to enjoy listening to all the different people who came through the playground at different times. We would have long talks, and arguments too.

My playground was in a city, where the streets were the only other places for children to be together out of doors. But even in many areas of the country-side now, the natural Adventure Playgrounds like my brook are

The hardest part is getting a patch of land you like, that is not being used for anything else at the moment. When you have found out who owns the land, they may listen to your ideas for a playground and allow it to be used as a playground for the time being. If it belongs to the Council, they may allow it to be used as a playground for ever; but if it belongs to a farmer or builder they may be able to spare it only for a limited time. It is a good idea to get a local councillor on your side, because the Council can help you

provide fencing, floodlights for dark winter evenings, a heated hut, and other materials. Local builders may help with bulldozers to make hills, sand for sandpits, and timber from demolished houses. A factory may have huge wooden crates to give away . . . and so on. The more people that are interested the better, and not just at the building stage; it is a good idea to keep a few adults interested in coming into the playground and doing things every now and then. For instance, if someone is building

a canoe in his garage, why can't he come and build it in the playground, so that everyone can watch?

In talking to some adults, you will often find that at first they will have certain arguments against Adventure Playgrounds. They will call them dirty, disorderly and dangerous. The answer is that there are fewer accidents in Adventure Playgrounds than in the playground at school with a hard floor. It is true that the high structures in an Adventure are a bit risky; but you seem to bear this in mind and take care. During the hours an Adventure is open, the other possible places to play — the streets — are much more dangerous. If you like, you can say going to the playground helps keep you off the streets and out of trouble. It stops you rampaging about the town breaking windows, terrorising citizens, stealing from shops, and getting run over!

Your job is not finished when you have succeeded in setting up a playground. There are always people aching to have it pulled down again, so that they can build an office, or plant a tidy garden or area of grass. To keep our playground open, we had to have a march of all the kids to the Town Hall, and make a big noise in the local newspapers.

Apart from that, there is always tons to do in a playground, to keep it a lively place where everyone keeps on wanting to come. You can have special events, like films and outings, or a barbecue on Bonfire Night. You can make things for the smaller kids, like see-saws and stepping stones, and crazy walks on a smaller scale than the big towers. You can erect climbing nets and cable cars, or you can come indoors and do a playground magazine or concert. But you will have plenty of ideas. In fact: why not put your ideas on paper and enter for the Competition on page 69.

'Last Line' Competition Results

Last year's *Magpie Annual* competition brought in a hilarious postbag. What we asked you to do was to complete five verses by adding a last line to each.

The judge was looking for three things: humour, inventiveness and aptness. Lots of the entries had the first two qualities but the lines of the winners had all three.

Here are the winning lines of **Nicholas Raistrick** (10 and under age group) and **Ann Bukowski** (over 10):

Nicholas   **Ann**

I thought I saw an antelope
On roller skates one day
I looked again and saw it was

A clever deer at play   **Two toothbrushes at play**

I thought I saw a mountain goat
Fall off a motor bike
I looked again and saw it was

A scarecrow in the dike   **A docker out on strike**

I thought I saw a schoolteacher
Who couldn't do his sums
I looked again and saw it was

Dad counting on his thumbs   **A monkey counting thumbs**

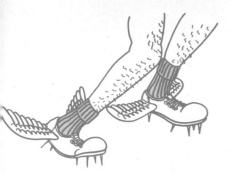

I thought I saw a premium bond
Go running down the street
I looked again and saw it was

Old Ernie's sprinting feet

A packet of puffed wheat

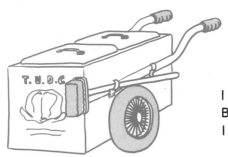

I thought I saw a limousine
Being driven by my Dad
I looked again and saw it was

A dust cart he once had

A Sultan from Baghdad

Nicholas Raistrick aged 9, from Morecambe in Lancashire, and Ann Bukowski, aged 13, from Dewsbury in Yorkshire, both appeared on Magpie to receive their prizes of a selection of books.

Runners-up
10 & under:
Janice Stones, Donald Ellwood, Timothy Sourlock, Elaine Binstead, Andrew Hamilton, Wendy Hewitt,

Jane Farrington, Jacqueline Cole, Thomas Williams, June Knight, Janice English, Rachel Crowhurst, Gail Harrison.
Over 10:
Fiona Claxton, Graham Lyper, Amanda Briggs, Jonathan Aldridge, Jennifer Hill, Katharine Spink, Alan Southgate, Leigh Brooks, Janice Linden, Elizabeth Wilson, Susan Birch.

Acknowledgments
For permission to reproduce illustrations Thames Television would like to thank: Janis Browne (*animal tracks drawings and writing, onion string, onion seller on bike, candle, sun dial and egg timer*), Ardea Photographics (*animal tracks photos*), Fox Photos Ltd (*grandfather clock*), The Guildhall Library (*Salisbury clock*), Science Museum, London—crown copyright (*Dondi clock*), The Illustrated London News (*Big Ben being dragged by horses*), Stephen Finch (*tote bag drawings*), Keystone Press Agency Ltd (*skiing and curling photos*), Barnaby's Picture Library (*skating photo*), Abelard-Schuman Ltd (*drawings from Jacques Carelman's "Catalogue of Extraordinary Objects"*), Hugh Routledge (*adventure playground photos*), Peter Lock (*"Last Line" cartoons*).
"The Forging of a Nation": drawn by Gerry Embleton, script by Angus Allan, lettering by Fred Allen. Victorian name brooches from the collection of Mrs Everna Zabell. Story illustrations by George Him.

Magpie team Randal Beattie (*producer*); Lesley Burgess (*associate producer*); Graeme Duckham, Richard Mervyn, Audrey Starrett, Peter Yolland (*directors*); Helen Best, Christie Brown, Ted Clisby, Martyn Day, Helen Dickinson, Samantha Hanson, Lois Lorant, Steve Timmins, Gill Trethowan (*researchers*); Dorothy Friend, Cherry Crompton, Sheila Stirrat (*production assistants*); Colin Barratt, Bob Oliver, Tony O'Toole, David Rush (*film editors*); Bernard Cooper, Ray Shepherd, John Wright (*assistant film editors*); Jean Lyall (*secretary*); Heather Meredith, Marita Samuels, Pat Wise (*Magpie mail*).

QUIZ

When you have read the **Magpie Annual**, you will know the answers to these questions.
(If stuck, see bottom of page.)

1 Who set the fashion for wearing a kimono instead of a teagown?

2 What was the dish that Duchamps did not serve for Christmas dinner?

3 What English name means 'noble' and 'bright'?

4 When and where were the first separate winter Olympic sports held?

5 Where can you see the Latin inscription 'Domine salvam fac reginam nostram Victoria primam'? And what does it mean?

6 In which year did the Romans, led by Julius Caesar, land in Britain?

7 Which badge will Magpie send you if you write a tall story?

8 What profession is carried out in England by sixty-four Frenchmen?

GET THE SHERIFF, QUICKLY — BILLY THE KID'S IN TOWN!

Answers: 1 Lady Randolph Churchill; **2** Terrine of thrushes; **3** Albert; **4** At Chamonix in 1924; **5** On Big Ben. 'O Lord save our queen Victoria the first.'; **6** AD 43; **7** Six for Gold; **8** Onion-selling.

ORANGE SURPRISE

Ingredients (for 6 people)
6 oranges
1 can frozen concentrated
orange juice
1 sachet gelatine
baby meringues or cream
angelica
water

Utensils
2 bowls
a glass
an orange squeezer
a grater
a knife
a spoon

Empty the gelatine into a glass and mix with $\frac{1}{4}$ pint water. Stand the glass in a bowl of hot water to melt the gelatine.

Cut the tops off the oranges and squeeze out all their juice. (Don't throw away the empty orange cases – you'll need them!)

Into a bowl pour the juice you have squeezed, the can of concentrated juice and the melted gelatine.

Grate the zest from the orange tops and add that too.

When the orange jelly mixture is almost set, fill each of the empty orange cases with it. Now put the cases in the freezer to ice.

Before serving your orange surprises, decorate them with angelica and whipped cream or meringues.

Monster Make-up

Make-up artists are involved in every programme that goes out on television, even when all they have to do is dab a bit of powder on a politician's nose so that it doesn't shine during an interview. But they really come into their own when asked to change completely the face of a character. Last year Launa Bradish showed you how Mick, the mildest of men, could be transformed into a maddening monster.

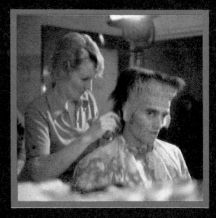

1. Mick, without make-up but with his hair pinned back ready for the transformation, looks slightly apprehensive.

2. Launa puts shadow in Mick's eye sockets to make his eyes look sunken. Then latex, a rubbery substance which sets and changes the contours of the face, is applied to indicate scars and stitching.

3. The head-piece with wig is fitted and crepe hair is stuck to Mick's neck-line to cover his own nape. The edges of the wig and the head-piece's side flaps are stuck down with spirit gum.

4. Latex, which is white while it's wet, is applied on top of the spirit gum.

5. The head-piece is now in place and it's just a question of building up the scar tissues with cotton wool and latex.

6. Now Mick has changed his costume, the scars have been finished off and make-up blood is inserted into his wounds.

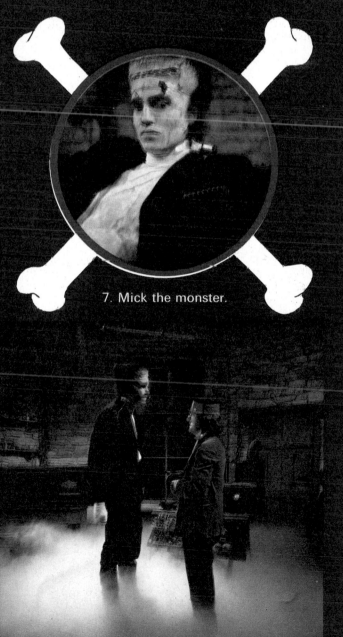

7. Mick the monster.

HOW MANY MAGPIE BADGES HAVE YOU GOT?

These are the Magpie Badges. You could own ten of them. Each one means that you have done something special. So why not see how many you can collect? This is what you have to do to get each badge.

One for Sorrow
If you have spent one night or more in hospital, let Magpie know, and ask your nurse or doctor or your parents to sign the letter.

The Original Magpie Badge
This badge is only given for an especially good letter or drawing or anything which has taken much more time and trouble than usual to complete. You cannot ask for this badge.

Two for Joy
When you have passed any sort of test or examination, write Magpie a letter and ask your teacher to sign it.

Three for a Girl and Four for a Boy
These badges are given to girls or boys who write an interesting letter to Magpie on any subject they choose. A good drawing or painting can also qualify for these badges.

Five for Silver
This is a very special badge. You are given it if you send in a really original idea for a Magpie programme item. Write in detail about how you think the item should be arranged for the programme, and if Magpie likes the idea, you will have earned the badge.

Six for Gold
All you have to do to qualify for this badge is send Magpie a tall story. preferably of your own invention.

Seven for a Secret Never to be Told
If you think that one of your friends has done a good deed, write and tell Magpie, giving your friend's name and address, and they will be sent the badge. You cannot nominate yourself, but if you have done a good deed you can always qualify for the badge by asking a friend to write about the deed to Magpie.

Nine for a Kiss
Jenny gives this badge to any boy or girl who has learnt to swim since 1 July 1970. Your letter should be signed by your parent or guardian.
Mick gives it to anyone who writes to him about a visit to an interesting place, such as a museum, historical building, art gallery etc. Tell him what you liked best about your visit, and what you learned from it.
Doug gives this badge to anyone who takes up a sport they have never done before, or who introduces a friend to a new sport.

Ten for a Bird You Must Not Miss
You can only be awarded this badge if you actually appear on Magpie.

Eight for a Wish
All runners up in Magpie competitions receive this badge.

ADVENTURE PLAYGROUND COMPETITION

What is your idea of a really exciting playground? Can you visualise a place where whatever your mood you can always find something exciting for you and your friends to do?

For this year's *Magpie Annual* competition, we'd like you to imagine such a place. Think of all the things you'd like to be able to do there. Then draw a plan of your ideal adventure playground. It doesn't matter if your drawing is not very good, but make clear what you would do in each part of the playground. The judge will be looking for a well thought out plan, imaginitive use of the area and scope for lots of interesting activities. Read the article on page 58 for ideas.

The competition is divided into two age groups: ten-and-under and over ten. The winners in each age group will be invited to appear on the Magpie programme to receive an exciting prize. Your entries should arrive no later than 31 January 1976. Send them, together with your name, age and address, to:
Adventure Playground Competition
Magpie
Thames Television
Teddington Lock
Middlesex

Editorial: **Alison Wade**
Design: **Sari Finch**

Magpie Annual 1976 © 1974, Thames Television

Printed and bound in Great Britain by
Jarrold & Sons Ltd, Cowgate, Norwich.

Published in Great Britain by World Distributors (Manchester) Ltd,
12 Lever Street, Manchester M60 1TS.
No material may be reproduced without the written consent of the publisher.
SBN 7235 0343 5